Communities and Ecosystems

Cover photo is of the southern Oregon coast at Gold Beach in the redwood belt, from *The Last Redwoods* by François Leydet, published by The Sierra Club. [Reproduced by permission of Philip Hyde, Box 220, Taylorsville, California.]

CURRENT CONCEPTS IN BIOLOGY
A Macmillan Series
NORMAN H. GILES, WALTER KENWORTHY, AND JOHN G. TORREY, Editors

Communities and Ecosystems

Robert H. Whittaker

Cornell University

The Macmillan Company,
Collier-Macmillan Limited, London

To Clara

First Printing

Library of Congress catalog card number: 73–77492

The Macmillan Company
Collier-Macmillan Canada, Ltd., Toronto, Ontario
Printed in the United States of America

Preface

ON THE SURFACE of the earth living organisms and their environments form a thin film, the biosphere. A pervasive interrelatedness of living things and environments to one another characterizes the biosphere. Organisms form interacting systems or communities, these communities are coupled to their environments by transfer of matter and energy, and communities and environments of the biosphere as a whole are related by movements of air, water, and organisms. The biosphere is man's environment, and man is now altering the biosphere in ways disadvantageous to himself. The importance of understanding the natural systems formed by organisms and environments for its own sake and for the sake of man's future is not always granted in a civilization guided by technology, despite the increasing emphasis of functional systems in technology.

The study of living systems in relation to environment is the science of ecology. Because of the wide range of concerns of ecology it is difficult to treat in a single book. In developing the Macmillan series "Current Concepts in Biology," it was thought better to prepare two books representing major divisions of the science. Much ecological understanding can be integrated around populations as living systems and the manner in which populations function in relation to environment; this aspect of ecology is the subject of *The Ecology of Populations* by Arthur S. Boughey. Much ecological understanding can be integrated also around the concepts of communities as assemblages of different species which interact with one another, and ecosystems as functional systems formed by communities and their environments. These aspects of ecology are dealt with in *Communities and Ecosystems*. The two books are designed to complement one another and to serve as introductions to ecology either separately or together. An additional important part of ecology is represented in the series by David E. Davis's *Integral Animal Behavior*. The reader will find the present book concerns the structure of natural communities, the function of ecosystems, and the problems of man's relations to the biosphere.

R. H. W.

Contents

5

Cycling and Pollution 105

6

Conclusion: Human Ecology 147

List of Figures

List of Tables

Introduction

IN NORTHERN CALIFORNIA and southern Oregon there are forests like no others—the great coastal redwood forests. Some twenty years ago, the author was drawn to study part of the ecology of these forests— their species composition and relation to other kinds of forests, their variation with topographic position and the climatic gradient from the fog belt inland, their evolutionary history and relation to the mixed, ancient forests that occurred across the continent in Tertiary time, and their dimensions compared with those of other forests. A redwood forest is a *natural community*, an assemblage of populations of plants, animals, bacteria, and fungi that live in an environment and interact with one another, forming together a distinctive living system with its own composition, structure, environmental relations, development, and function. A redwood forest or an oak forest, a piece of prairie or a patch of desert—each of these may be approached as a community, a system of organisms living together and linked together by their effects on one another and their responses to the environment they share.

In each case the community has a close-linked, interacting relation to environment, as climate and soil affect the community and the community affects the soil and its own internal climate or microclimate, as energy and matter are taken from environment to run the community's living function and form its substance, transferred from one organism to another in the community, and released back to environment. A community and its environment treated together as a functional system of complementary relationships, and transfer and circulation of energy and matter, is an *ecosystem*. Thus a redwood forest is an ecosystem that can be characterized as different in some degrees from other forests in its structure, its particular adaptation to

1

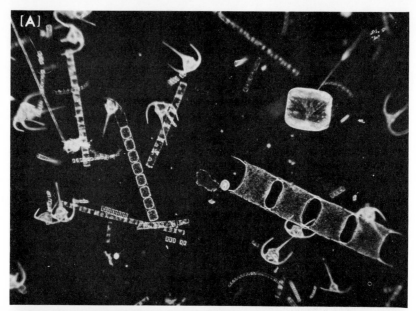

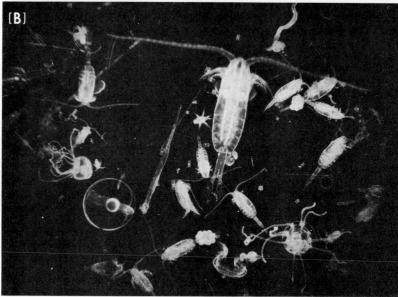

Figure 1·1. Marine plankton organisms. A: Plant plankton magnified 65 times. Most of the cells are diatoms (the large chain of four is *Biddulphia sinensis,* the smaller chains *Stephanopyxis turris* and *Rhizosolenia faeröense,* the single large cell *Coscinodiscus concinnus*); the cells with curved spines are dinoflagellates (*Ceratium tripos*). **B:** Animal plankton magnified 16 times. The shrimplike animals with long antennae are copepods (one large individual of *Calanus finmarchicus,* a number of smaller *Pseudocalanus elongatus,* and a larval copepod just to the left of the large *Calanus*). An arrow worm (*Sagitta*) parallels the large copepod on its left, and the figure includes also two small jellyfish, two tunicates (*Oikopleura,* curly organisms near the top and bottom), and a fish egg (circular object). Chains of diatom cells may be seen on the right.

[Both photographs are of organisms in the living condition concentrated in sea water, taken by electronic flash. Copyright by Douglas P. Wilson, see also A. Hardy, *The Open Sea.*]

a humid coastal environment and effects on its own microclimate, its manner of utilizing sunlight energy in high productivity, and its way of circulating nutrients between the soil and the organisms of the community.

Offshore from the redwoods are very different communities. In the surface waters of the sea there is a community at the opposite extreme of size from the redwood forests—the plankton, an almost invisible community of microorganisms. The plankton is a full community of green plants, animals feeding on these and predatory animals feeding on other animals, bacteria, and fungi (Figure 1·1), organisms that are suspended in the water and carried passively by currents. These organisms are in intimate chemical relation to the water as materials circulate from water through the organisms and back to water; the plankton with its aquatic environment is an ecosystem. It is possible, observing sea water without a microscope, to be unaware of the plankton in it, but the marine plankton is the most widespread kind of natural community on the earth's surface.

The area of the author's study in the redwood belt has changed in the last twenty years. The area was then relatively remote and lightly used by man, reached by winding roads above the sea that passed extensive uncut forests and largely unoccupied shores. As we see it today the forests are smaller remnants, the towns are larger, and the human use of the area ever heavier. There are other ecological changes: along much of the coast the richness of the shore life and inshore fishing is reduced; populations of some of the large predatory birds of the coast are in decline; smog appears at times in valleys with cities far smaller than Los Angeles; and the sardines that were fished by fleets of boats from Alaska to California and were the basis of one of the country's major fishery industries have decreased, overfished despite warnings about danger of depleting the population, to near-disappearance.

If one visits a beach of the area now, in the evening, the glare of the lights of increasing traffic on a fast coastal highway contrasts with the softly luminous moving lines of the surf, which at times glows with the phosphorescence of a plankton organism, a dinoflagellate doubtless even more ancient as a type than the redwood. The seacoast, where many of the richest and most productive of natural communities are concentrated and where man is concentrating much of his population, thus juxtaposes not only the natural realms of the land and sea, but also two disparate orders: man's current ways of aggressively expanding technology and use of environment, and the evolutionarily old, vulnerable, natural order of communities and ecosystems.

Man necessarily uses environments and harvests from communities, but many of the changes brought by man in doing so are unforeseen and against his choice and interests. There is reason for concern now not only with unwanted changes in natural conditions, but with the implications to man himself of these changes. There is great need that man's use of environment should be based on models different from that of the Pacific sardine fisheries—exploitation expanding, uncontrolled by foresight, to the eventual destruction of the resource and of the institution exploiting it. The foresight should be directed by an understanding of ecosystems and of the world-ecosystem that is man's environment.

Ecology is the area of the biological sciences that is concerned with living systems in their environmental contexts. In practice the living systems studied by ecologists are those of the highest levels of organization—individual organisms, populations, societies (as organizations of individuals of one species), communities (as systems of populations usually of many species), and ecosystems. Difficulties and challenges of ecology result from the effort to deal with the complexities of these higher organic systems, in which biological processes of lower levels are integrated with physical and chemical processes of environment into phenomena that are distinctive to the higher system—and must be interpreted in terms of the function of that system.

Because of the breadth of the phenomena with which ecology deals, it is convenient to recognize two major divisions or levels. The first of these, *autecology,* concerns the ecology of populations and their individual organisms, and includes as fields of study physiological ecology, genecology, population dynamics, animal behavior, and the study of symbioses. These fields concern primarily one species at a time (or in symbiosis and often in population dynamics two or a few species). The other area of ecology concerns systems of many species—whole communities or major fractions of communities, and ecosystems. This area of study is termed *synecology* in the English-speaking countries, *biocenology* or *biosociology* by many Europeans; and it includes studies of terrestrial ecosystems, biological aspects of oceanography, limnology as the study of lakes and streams, biogeochemistry as the study of circulation of materials in the world ecosystem, and applied problems of man's management and alteration of ecosystems. This book is designed as an introduction to synecology, and its discussion will proceed from the structure of communities, to relations of communities with environment, to energy function in community production, to the circulation of materials in ecosystem function, to pollution processes and implications for human ecology.

References

Bates, Marston. (1960) *The Forest and the Sea.* New York: Random House. 277 pp.

Boughey, Arthur S. (1968) *Ecology of Populations.* New York: Macmillan. viii + 135 pp.

Buchsbaum, Ralph, and Mildred Buchsbaum. (1957) *Basic Ecology.* Pittsburgh: Boxwood Press. ix + 192 pp.

Odum, Eugene P. (1963) *Ecology.* New York: Holt, Rinehart & Winston. vii + 152 pp.

2

Community Structure and Composition

Physiognomy and Growth-Forms

THE STUDY OF THE FORMS and structures of organisms is the science of morphology. It is an important area of biology, more important than is often recognized in current writing that takes for granted the knowledge of morphology built by generations of biologists. It is primarily by form and structure that living things are classified, by which their adaptations to environment are recognized, and by which evolutionary relationships are known or surmised. It is by movement of research through the study of structure into the study of function related to that structure that much of the development of physiological and chemical biology has occurred. In our concern with natural communities it is appropriate that we first consider aspects of their structure, and then proceed to their environmental relations and functions. Study of form and structure in natural communities is termed not morphology but *physiognomy*.

The structure of the plankton community is usually invisible, which is not to say nonexistent. In adaptation to the free-floating life, most plankton organisms are microscopic and short-lived or rapidly multiplying. There is no accumulation of massive structure, and the physiognomy of a plankton community is limited to a rather sparse and changeable dispersion of microorganisms in water. More impressive physiognomy appears in communities of organisms on or attached to the bottom of the sea—in giant kelp beds, the elaboration of forms and colors of coral reefs, and the patterns of distinctive starlike, plumelike, fanlike, and flowerlike animals on the deep ocean bottom. It is in the study of communities on land, however, that physiognomy has been most discussed and most rewarding.

To describe the forms of communities on land one needs to characterize major kinds of form in plants, for physiognomy results from the forms of the plants that make up the community. The classes or kinds of form in plants are referred to as *growth-forms*. A number of characteristics of plants—height, woody versus herbaceous or nonwoody growth, stem form, leaf form, and leaf deciduousness or evergreenness, and so on—are used to define growth-forms. The growth-forms do not (with a few exceptions in some systems) correspond to the units into which systematists classify plants. There are a number of systems of growth-forms, one of which is outlined in Table 2·1. The list is not complete, but limited to those growth-forms most important in determining community structure.

TABLE 2·1
Major Plant Growth-Forms on Land

Trees, larger woody plants, mostly well above three meters tall
    Needle-leaved (mainly conifers—pine, spruce, larch, redwood, and so on)
    Broad-leaved evergreen (many tropical and subtropical trees, mostly with medium-sized leaves)
    Evergreen-sclerophyll (with smaller, tough, evergreen leaves)
    Broad-leaved deciduous (leaves shed in the Temperate Zone winter, or in the tropical dry season)
    Thorn-trees (armed with spines, in many cases with compound, deciduous leaves)
    Rosette trees (unbranched, with a crown of large leaves—palms and tree-ferns)
Lianas (woody climbers or vines)
Shrubs, smaller woody plants, mostly below three meters in height
    Broad-leaved deciduous
    Evergreen-sclerophyll
    Rosette shrubs (yucca, agave, aloe, palmetto, and so on)
    Stem succulents (cacti, certain euphorbias, and so on)
    Thorn-shrubs
    Semishrubs (suffrutescent, that is, with the upper parts of stems and branches dying back in unfavorable seasons)
    Subshrubs or dwarf-shrubs (low shrubs spreading near the ground surface, less than 25 cm. high)
Epiphytes (plants growing wholly above the ground surface, on other plants)
Herbs, plants without perennial aboveground woody stems
    Ferns
    Graminoids (grasses, sedges, and other grasslike plants)
    Forbs (herbs other than ferns and graminoids)
Thallophytes
    Lichens
    Mosses
    Liverworts

Vertical Structure

Most communities show vertical differentiation or stratification—different species occur at different heights above the ground, or depths below the water surface. The species have different positions along a vertical gradient of depth in the community and decreasing light intensity. Intensity of light necessarily decreases from the surface of the community, which is in full sunlight, downward; light absorption by the organisms themselves is a principal reason for this extinction of light with depth. In a forest one may observe a several-storied physiognomy with a number of growth-forms (in each of which there may be a number of species) occurring one above the other to form the community's vertical structure.

The forest trees, with their upper foliage in full sunlight, form the canopy or uppermost level (Figure 2·1). The leaves and branch surfaces of the canopy trees may absorb and scatter more than half of the sunlight energy, but beneath the canopy there is a lower layer of smaller trees utilizing some of the remaining light. This lower tree stratum usually contains both younger individuals of the canopy tree species, and mature trees of other, smaller species that do not normally reach canopy height. Less than 10 per cent of the sunlight reach-

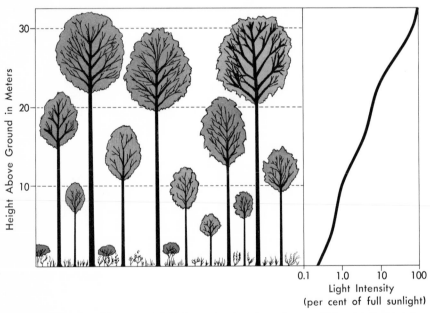

Figure 2·1. Stratification and light extinction in a forest. Different species of trees, shrubs, and herbs bear foliage at different heights above ground (left) and are adapted to life at different light intensities (right), which result from the absorption of sunlight by that foliage.

ing the upper canopy may penetrate through the tree foliage of both levels, and spectral composition of the remaining internal light of the forest is changed from that of sunlight. Species of a third level of vegetation, shrubs, are adapted to utilizing this weaker light within the forest, further reducing the light that reaches herbs beneath the shrub layer. The remaining light (1 to 5 per cent of incident sunlight in many forests) supports the growth of the herb layer. Beneath the herbs, mosses on the ground may form still another vegetation layer. In some dense forests only a fraction of 1 per cent of incident sunlight reaches the forest floor.

A forest tree may gain advantage by reaching the canopy, where abundant sunlight supports photosynthesis, but the tree must spend much of the energy of photosynthesis in growth of the woody tissue of stem and branches to support the foliage in the canopy. There may be apparent disadvantage in the low light intensities in which the forest herbs must live, but the herb need not spend its more modest photosynthetic profit on woody supporting tissue. Forest structure involves a gradient of growth-forms—upper and lower trees, upper and lower shrubs, upper and lower herbs, and soil-surface mosses—in adaptation to the gradient of light intensity. Along the gradient growth-form designs change from one extreme (the upper tree with foliage in full sunlight, massive supporting stem and branch structure, and a root system smaller in mass than the aboveground structure) to herbs with adaptations at the other extreme (photosynthesis at low levels of light intensity, small investment in aboveground supporting structure, and accumulation of reserve food in a root system more massive than the aboveground structure).

Even as different plant species are adapted to different positions in this vertical gradient, so different animal species also occupy different levels in the forest. Different groups of bird species, for example, may be found feeding and nesting near the ground, in the shrub and small-tree foliage beneath the canopy, and in the canopy itself. Different arthropod species occur at different levels from the canopy downward to the herb stratum and to and below the ground surface. A group of animals—mites and springtails, millepedes and centipedes, ground beetles, and so on—occur primarily in the leaf-litter on the soil surface; these animals, which are seldom seen on the surface by daylight are the *cryptozoans*. Other animals occur at different depths in the soil, in which different plant species also have their roots extending to different depths.

In the plankton too there is a degree of vertical differentiation in the adaptation of different species to different levels and light intensities. Vertical movements affect the distribution of these species, however, and vertical differences in the community are less evident than in the forest. Communities of lighted zones below tide levels on the ocean floor show a differentiation determined in part by light intensities. Vertical differentiation is thus a common feature of many natural communities. So also is a degree of horizontal differentiation.

Horizontal Pattern

We say that plants form a carpet on the forest floor, but this is a carpet with its own kind of pattern. Suppose we lay out one hundred randomly located quadrats or plots, each 1 meter square, on the forest floor and record the undergrowth plants present in each of these. We can then ask two kinds of questions about the pattern.

First, are the individual plants scattered on the forest floor at random, or are they to some degree grouped or clustered? As a basis for answering the question, consider occurrence in plots of a hypothetical species whose individuals are randomly distributed and whose foliage covers a small fraction of the forest floor. A Poisson distribution is appropriate to describe the numbers of individual plants in plots—61 plots with no plants of the species, 30 with 1, 8 with 2, and 1 with 3, say, for 50 individual plants in 100 plots. (The Poisson distribution for an ideal case of random distribution of individuals may be described by

$$f = e^{-m}, me^{-m}, \frac{m^2 e^{-m}}{2!}, \frac{m^3 e^{-m}}{3!}, \ldots.$$

Hence, for our example,

$$F = \Sigma 100 f = 60.6 + 30.3 + 7.6 + 1.2 + 0.16 + \ldots.$$

F is the total number of plots, f the relative (decimal) frequencies of plots containing 0, 1, 2, 3, ... individuals, m the mean number of individuals per plot (0.5 in the example), and e the base of natural logarithms.)

The numbers of individuals in plots will fit the Poisson distribution only if the distribution of individuals is random—if the location of each individual is determined by factors independent of those determining the location of other individuals. This is seldom the case. The factors may tend to cause individuals to grow close to one another, to be clumped into groups. If the individuals are clumped, the pattern of numbers of individuals on plots will be shifted: there will be more plots with larger numbers of individuals, and hence also more plots with none, for a given total number of individuals. The clumped distribution is termed *contagious*. A chi-square measurement can be used to test the significance of the difference between an actual distribution of numbers of individuals in plots, and a Poisson distribution calculated for the same number of individuals and plots. There are a number of approaches to measuring degree of contagion, for distributions that depart significantly from the Poisson series. One may, for example, use the ratio of the variance to the mean. Because the variance of a Poisson distribution is equal to its mean, this ratio for a random distribution is one. A ratio significantly above one implies contagious or clumped dstribution, a ratio less than one implies that individuals are more evenly spaced than a random distribution would imply. The condition in which individuals tend to be evenly spaced, rather than scattered at random, is termed *negative contagion* or *regularity* (Figure 2·2).

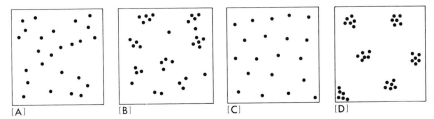

Figure 2·2. Four ways in which individuals of a population can be distributed in horizontal space in a community. A: Random dispersion (note its apparent irregularity). **B:** A clumped or contagious distribution. **C:** A regular or negatively contagious distribution. **D:** A combination of strong clumping of individuals into colonies, and regular distribution of the colonies as wholes.

Regularity is apparently uncommon and difficult to demonstrate in natural communities. Some plants appear to have rather even distributions, among them the shrubs in some deserts in which it is reasonable to suppose that it is less probable that one shrub will be close to another shrub of the same species (hence within the area of its root effects) than farther away from it. Singing birds divide a community into territories, and each male of a species establishes and defends an area in which the pair nests and feeds; these territories may be of the same order of size for all pairs of a given species in the community. It seems clear that interaction among the birds has brought about a distribution that is more regular than random. It may be difficult, however, with either desert shrubs or singing birds to demonstrate statistically that the distribution is regular.

Departures from randomness toward positive contagion are very common indeed and easily established by measurement. It may be quite apparent that the plants of the forest floor are concentrated in patches, with few individuals between the patches. There may be at least three reasons for such patches:

1. Dispersal from parent plants. Seeds from a plant may fall near that plant, producing when the seeds grow a clump of young plants. Plants spreading from a parent plant by runners or rhizomes may form clumps of individuals, or of aboveground stems that are still connected.

2. Differences in environment. The forest floor is a mosaic of patches receiving more light, or less, through the canopy. Light differences among these patches may influence the development of patches of herbs. A microrelief of scarcely visible rises and depressions, or other obscure patches of soil characteristics, also may contribute to the formation of undergrowth patches.

3. Species interrelations. One species may be dependent on another (for example, an herb parasitic on the roots of a tree species), or an herb population may be denser under trees of a given species because of the effects of the trees on the soil. Patches of the herb species may then occur around or under the tree species; the herb species can be contagiously distributed whether or not the tree species is. If major species form clumps from which some minor species are excluded, then these minor species will have nonrandom distributions concentrated in the spaces between the clumps of the major species.

Clearly, these three causes of contagion may be combined with one another in various ways. Effects of the first of the causes may (in the absence of the other two) tend to even out toward a random distribution, given sufficient time. The second and third, however, imply differentiation of the community in horizontal space.

Animal populations too show varying degrees of contagion. Marine plankton animals and fish may be strongly clumped into schools. These clumps are not easily studied, for the investigator is using equipment lowered into the ocean to take measurements on a population whose presence cannot usually be seen from the surface, whose boundaries cannot be effectively located, and which is changing its distribution in time even as it is sampled. The problem is suggestive of fishing for a cloud, but location of populations by echo sounding and other techniques will aid in studying them. Patchiness in terrestrial animal communities is more easily investigated. Most of the smaller animals of the forest are likely to show contagious distributions, with the degrees of contagion ranging up to the very strong contagion of ants in their colonies. Each species may have its own degree of clumping and spacing of clumps, different from the patterns of other species.

One asks, in consequence, a second answer from our forest plots:

TABLE 2·2
Occurrence of Two Species in 100 Sample Plots

	Species B, present	absent	
Species A, present	$a = 17$	$b = 22$	$a + b = 39$
absent	$c = 13$	$d = 48$	$c + d = 61$
	$a + c = 30$	$b + d = 70$	$F = 100$

Chi-square test of species association

$$\chi^2 = \frac{[(ad - bc) - 0.5F]^2 \times F}{(a + b)(a + c)(b + d)(c + d)} = 4.6 \ (p < 0.05).$$

Coefficient of association of Cole (1949), for case when $ad \geqslant bc$

$$C_a = \frac{ad - bc}{(a + b)(b + d)} = 0.194$$

how the distributions of different species are related to one another. The undergrowth plots may be studied again to determine correlations among the species occurring in them. One may set up a simple table of the numbers of plots containing one, or both, or neither of a pair of species (Table 2·2). A chi-square test can indicate the probability that the two species are distributed independently, or are associated with one another. As indicated in Table 2·2, the example gives a chi-square of 4.6, which implies (with one degree of freedom) a probability of less than 0.05 that species A and B are independently distributed. The distributional association of the two species is significant, though it probably would not be recognized in the field (more individuals of A occur outside, than in, plots containing B). Other measurements, which range from 0 (for species distributed independently of one another) to 1.0 (complete distributional association or correspondence) and -1.0 (complete disassociation or avoidance), can be used to express degrees of distributional association. One of these measurements (Table 2·2) gives a value of 0.194 for the statistically significant but relatively weak association of species A and B. The degree of association may also in some circumstances be measured by comparing numbers of individuals of the two species in the plots, by rank correlation.

Correlations or associations between species are for the most part not strong, and many pairs of species in a community may show none. Among the species of a community, however, there will usually be some that are positively associated and tend to occur together, and some that are negatively associated and tend to occur separately. Parasites and insects which feed on a single plant species may be expected to show association with their host or food species. Positive associations may imply either that species are linked by the dependence of one on another, or that they are responding in similar ways to the small-scale differences of environment within the community. Negative associations may imply either that one species tends to exclude another by some effect on its population, or that the two species respond in different ways to the differences in environment.

Thus both differences in environment and interactions among species may be responsible for both contagion of individual species and association between species. Contagion and species association are related phenomena. Each species in the community has its own pattern of population distribution, often correlated with the patterns of other species and yet usually not quite like the pattern of any other species. When one conceives of the forest in terms of superimposed, different distributions of dozens of plant species and hundreds of animal species, the complexity and subtlety of pattern of the community may be evident. It is most to the point for our concerns that there is, in fact, marked horizontal differentiation within most communities, and that different species have different relations to this horizontal pattern.

Time Relations

We have been discussing differentiation of communities in space, but there is also differentiation in time. Environments of natural communities are rhythmic: in most environments light, temperature, and other environmental factors go through daily and yearly cycles. In some communities, especially those of ocean shores, there are also complex rhythms set by the rise and fall of tides. Physiology and behavior of organisms respond to rhythms of environment in many cases by linkage or coupling with environmental rhythm by an intrinsic, functional rhythm of the organism. We may expect rhythms of function in natural communities in adaptation to rhythms of environment.

Many plankton animals, both of fresh water and the oceans, migrate up and down in daily cycles (Figure 2·3). In a common pattern of movement the plankton sink, or swim downward, as light increases in the morning so that most individuals remain below the zone of most intense light near the surface. After remaining at some depth during the daylight hours they swim upward as light decreases in late afternoon and evening, to spend the night in the water nearer the surface. A marked rhythm thus also affects the plant plankton, which grows most actively in the sunlight hours, and may be harvested most effectively by animals in the nighttime hours. Patterns of movement may be quite different, however, among the species of a given plankton community. Distance of migration may range from centimeters in uni-

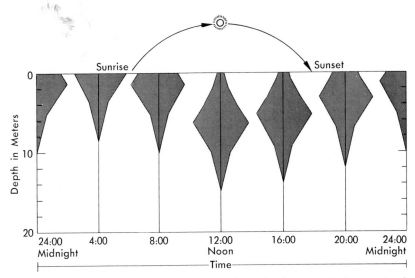

Figure 2·3. A pattern of vertical migration for a freshwater plankton animal.
Individuals move a few meters up and down in daily cycles, and the population as a
whole shifts downward below the most strongly lighted water in the daytime, upward
toward the surface at night. Widths of the polygons are relative numbers of individuals
at different depths.

cellular flagellates to many meters in the larger marine plankton animals. Populations of some of these as they move up and down in the
ocean are responsible for the deep scattering layer that reflects sound
waves transmitted through the water by sonar or echo sounding devices
to determine depth of the bottom. An animal population may produce
a reflection or apparent sonar bottom that is not merely false, but
mobile in daily cycles.

Plankton populations fluctuate rapidly in many water bodies, with
species replacing one another in periods of days and weeks. A number
of major species may occur as plankton dominants in the course of the
year. Thus in freshwater lakes species of diatoms and other yellow-green
algae may predominate in the winter plankton. As water temperatures
warm in later spring and early summer, these are replaced by desmids
and other green algae. At peak summer temperatures blue-green
algae may predominate or share dominance with the green algae; as
temperatures cool dominance shifts back toward the green and yellow-
green algae. Each species has an inactive stage in which it survives the
season unfavorable for its activity. Each species has its own place in
the annual pattern, determined by its own response to the fluctuations
of temperature and other environmental factors. The plankton community shows differentiation in time: different groups of species occur
at different times during the seasonal cycle. The year-round total

number of plankton species is much larger than the number present at a given time.

Seasonal and daily differentiation occurs also in forests. One group of insects are active in the daytime, another group at night, and a third group may be active in the twilight transitions of morning and evening. In terrestrial communities flycatchers, warblers, and other insectivorous birds are active by day, bats at night, and nighthawks in the dusk. Progress of the seasons is marked by the appearance of different groups of plants in flower and different groups of insects visiting these flowers. In deciduous forests spring beauties, dogtooth violets, and other herbs develop their foliage and flower early, before the trees are in leaf. Other groups of species have their maximum growth and flowering in later spring and in summer; still others, among them asters and golden-rods, grow and flower in later summer and fall.

Niche Difference

It appears that each species has its own time and place in the community, different from those of other species. There is much evolutionary interest in this observation.

We may choose to distinguish three aspects of the relations of a species to environment. The *area* of a species is its geographic range, its distribution in space as this may be plotted on a map. The *habitat* of the species refers to the kind of environment the species occurs in, as this environment may be described in physical and chemical terms and often by elevation, topographic position, and so on. A species may occupy a range of somewhat different habitats, or more than one distinctive kind of habitat, in different parts of its area. Thus pitch pine (*Pinus rigida*) in the eastern United States occurs on steep, rocky, dry, south-facing slopes at middle elevations in the Appalachian Mountains in the southern part of its area; on level, sandy, coastal plains in the northern part of its area; and in other habitats in still other parts of its area. Within each habitat one may describe for a species its position in the space, time, and functional relationships of the natural community that occupies that habitat. The species' place in a community in relation to other species is its *niche*.

Niche is thus a term for the specialization of a species population within a community. It is not irrelevant to recall the advantage of specialization in human societies. An individual may gain from professional specialization because of a high degree of skill or efficiency in his trade that ensures his obtaining the resources (income) he needs for his life. Two or more individuals may gain by following different specialties because they are not in competition, and each has his own assured source of income. The society at large may gain because the members' specializations serve one anothers' needs, and because the efficiency of the whole gains from the efficiency of the different specialists in their trades. It is hardly to be doubted that evolutionary advantage underlies the specializations we observe in natural communities.

There may be advantage to individuals, or species, in the choice of different specializations by which they avoid direct competition. By *competition* we mean a situation in which there is not enough of an environmental resource for both of two individuals, or two species populations. Use of the resource by one individual or species reduces the resource available to the other, and the growth or survival of the other is affected by shortage of the resource. (Or both may be affected by the competition.) Thus a young tree growing in the shade of a larger tree suffers from competitive limitation of the light available to it; the young tree will in consequence grow slowly, and it may die. A shrub population growing in the shade of a canopy tree population is limited in its growth because most of the sunlight is used or intercepted by the trees, and only a fraction of it reaches the shrubs. It may be true both that the shrubs are physiologically adapted to grow and reproduce successfully at this light intensity and that the shrub population could be much denser in the absence of trees competing with the shrubs for light.

We may seek to learn by experiment the consequences of direct competition between species. Two species that are closely equivalent in their niches are introduced in equal numbers into an experimental chamber. In classic experiments by Gause two species of *Paramecium* were introduced into cultures with bacteria for food and essentially constant environment. No two species will be identical in population functions: one will have some advantage expressed as a higher rate of survival and reproduction than the other, in a given set of environmental conditions. The experimental chamber can support only so many paramecia on the average. Within this essentially fixed combined population ceiling set by resources, one species increases its numbers, while the other must decline toward eventual extinction in the culture (Figure 2·4).

(The process may be described by equations developed by Gause (and by Volterra and Lotka). If environmental resources are not limiting, a population may increase geometrically: $dN/dt = rN$, in which the rate of growth in numbers of individuals (dN/dt) equals the number of individuals (N) in the population at a given time, times r as an intrinsic rate of increase for that population in the absence of crowding or competition effects on its growth. If environmental resources are limited, growth of the population will be slowed by competition with increasing effectiveness the more closely the number of individuals approaches the maximum number the environment

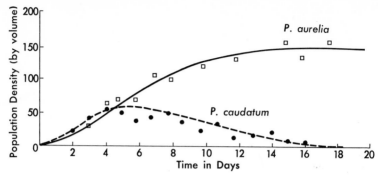

Figure 2·4. Competition in a closed culture between two *Paramecium* species.
The two species are direct competitors, and one of them declines to extinction in the
culture. [After Gause, 1934.]

can support. This maximum number is the carrying capacity of the
environment, K. The logistic curve is a convenient first approximation
for growth of a population to a ceiling level set by a limiting environment

$$\frac{dN}{dt} = rN\left(\frac{K - N}{K}\right)$$

In this, $(K - N)/K$ specifies that population growth will be reduced
as population number, N, approaches carrying capacity, K, and will
be zero when $N = K$; the population is then stabilized at carrying
capacity.

(The form of the logistic equation may now be applied to two
competing populations:

$$\frac{dN_1}{dt} = r_1N_1\frac{K_1 - N_1 - \alpha N_2}{K_1}$$

$$\frac{dN_2}{dt} = r_2N_2\frac{K_2 - N_2 - \beta N_1}{K_2}$$

In these, N_1 and N_2 are the populations of species 1 and 2 at a given
time, r_1 and r_2 are their intrinsic rates of population increase, and K_1
and K_2 are the environmental resource limits or carrying capacities
for each species in the absence of the other. The α and β are competition coefficients that express, through αN_2 and βN_1, the effects on
the population change of one species of the population level of the
other species.

(The equations imply that, for most relations of α and β to each
other and to K_1 and K_2, one species population will increase while the

other declines, until at equilibrium the latter is extinct. There is, however, another possibility. In the case that $\alpha < K_1/K_2$ and $\beta < K_2/K_1$, species 1 and 2 can survive at equilibrium in one another's presence. This is the case in which each species inhibits the growth of its own population more than that of the other population. This case occurs when the species have so divided environmental space that competition is more effective among individuals of each species within its own part of the space, than it is among individuals representing the two species.)

Simplified as such equations are from what happens in a natural community, certain inferences may be drawn. If two species are direct competitors, utilizing the same resources in the same space at the same time, then in the equilibrium condition one species will become extinct. If, however, the two species differ in their requirements or relation to space, then it is possible for them to coexist in a durable population balance. For *space,* in application to a community, read *niche.* The species can coexist if they differ in horizontal or vertical space requirement in the community, in time relation, in resources utilized or kind of interaction with other species—if they differ in niche.

We may further judge that the space, or niche, requirements of the two species need not be discontinuous, but may overlap. The species may be partial competitors. Individuals of the two species may compete, and yet each species has a fraction of experimental space or community niche in which it has a competitive advantage over the other species. This condition can be represented in an experiment by providing a refuge from which one species (the more effective competitor of the two) is wholly or partly excluded. The two populations may still meet and compete for resources in the rest of the experimental chamber, but the weaker species survives, with its refuge as a center of competitive advantage, in the presence of the stronger. The weaker species survives by virtue of its difference of niche from the stronger species.

The idea that two species cannot coexist permanently in the same niche is known as the *principle of Gause* (though a number of scientists contributed to its formulation). We may apply the idea to communities in the form of three statements, linked in a progression: (1) If two species occupy the same niche in the same stable community, one will become extinct. (2) No two species observed in a stable community are direct competitors: the species differ in niche requirements in ways that reduce competition between them. (3) The community is a system of interacting, niche-differentiated species populations that tend to complement one another, rather than directly competing, in their utilization of the community's space, time, resources, and possible kinds of interactions.

Much of what was said about variety of growth-forms in communities takes enhanced meaning from the concept of niche differentiation. The differences of growth-form among plants in a community are visible indications of the niche differentiation of these plants. Their niche differences should involve, however, a wide range of functional relations—in physiology, life cycle, and adaptation to other species— of which only a few have visible expression in growth-form.

Diversification of niches among the species of a community has evolved because of the selective disadvantage to one or both species of direct competition, versus the selective advantage (reliable availability of a distinct set of resources to support a given species, relatively free from competition for these resources by other species) of niche difference. For a pair of species and a single niche characteristic, one may represent the selective process as in Figure 2·5. The two populations

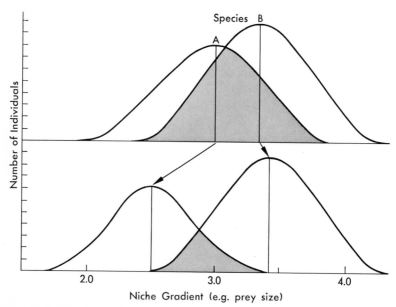

Figure 2·5. Selective niche divergence of two species. Above, two species overlap broadly in a niche characteristic, such as the mean prey-size choice by individuals. Competition reduces survival of individuals choosing prey of sizes around 3.0, hence selects against genes determining such prey choice. Below, mean prey-size adaptations have diverged, as indicated by the arrows connecting the mean prey-size choices for the species.

at first overlap broadly in a niche characteristic—sizes of prey taken by predatory or hunting animals, say. Individuals of each species have a genetically determined mean food-size preference, and when individuals of B are competing with individuals of A for the same food, A has an advantage over B. The survival of individuals of B adapted to prey sizes within the shaded overlap is lower than survival of individuals adapted to prey sizes outside this overlap and hence free of competition with A. The frequency of genes adapting B to prey sizes where it is in competition with A decreases relative to frequency of genes adapting B to capture of smaller prey. The mean genetic composition of the population of B shifts (and that of A may also shift) until the species, though they may still overlap in prey choice, are adapted to reliance on quite different sizes of animals for food.

It may be true, though it is difficult to establish, that a community as a system of niche-differentiated species can utilize environmental resources more efficiently for higher long-term productivity than a "community" of a single plant species. It seems that much of the relative stability of the animal populations in some communities is a consequence of diversity of species, variously interacting in their different niche roles, tending in various ways to limit and stabilize one another's populations. Communities with small numbers of species (for example, the arctic tundra) seem in general to be less stable than communities with larger numbers of species. Niche differentiation has become a central idea in the interpretation of natural communities. However, two aspects of the implications of niche differentiation for community structure remain to be considered: (1) How do species compare with one another in relative importance in a given community? (2) How do communities compare with one another in the numbers of species they include?

Niche Space and Species Importance

Some niche characteristics, such as prey size, can be quantified. We may consider growth-forms in the Sonoran desert of the lower mountain slopes in southeastern Arizona, a spectacular high desert of giant cactus, ocotillo, palo verde, and a great variety of plants (Figure $2\cdot6$). Occupation of niche space in this community involves first the relation of species to the vertical height axis. The heights at which plant species bear the greater part of their foliage range from near-zero in herbs with stems and leaves on the ground surface, to a few centimeters in other herbs, to a few decimeters in most of the semishrubs, to 0.5 to 2.0 meters in true shrubs of different species, to 2 to 5 meters in arborescent shrubs (ocotillo, palo verde, mesquite), whereas the giant cactus or saguaro has a photosynthetic surface to the top of its stem, up to 6 to 9 meters. Average position of the buds or tissues that survive unfavorable seasons and from which the foliage develops, from the ground surface up (or in some herbs below the ground surface), provides a convenient expression of plant height.

A second set of niche relationships involve seasonal time. There are two rainy seasons in this desert, one in winter and one in late summer, separated by dry seasons, and two waves of plant growth correspond

Figure 2·6. A Sonoran desert community of highly mixed growth-form composition. Taken near Tucson, Arizona, with the Santa Catalina Mountains in the background. The giant cacti are the saguaro, *Carnegiea gigantea*. [Courtesy of and copyright by W. A. Niering.]

to the rainy seasons. Among the perennial plants most utilize the moisture of both rainy seasons, but in different patterns of leaf and stem photosynthesis, patterns expressed in growth-forms and the seasonal behavior of foliage. The plants may again be arranged along a gradient, from those with persistent, evergreen leaves, through semideciduous species with leaves (or the leaf-bearing twigs of the semishrubs) persistent through less severe dry seasons but not more severe ones, to the deciduous mesquite, palo verde, and semishrubs. These in turn grade into forms like ocotillo, with short-lived leaves quickly produced and soon lost after rains, to the cacti, which lack leaves. In plants of the latter part of this sequence the stems and branches are green and photosynthesize to supplement the photosynthesis by the leaves; in the cacti photosynthesis is wholly by stem and branches. The plants form, then, a gradient of decreasing leaf persistence and increasing stem and branch photosynthesis, and we shall assume that differences along the gradient are significant in relation to plant competition. The gradient is also one of adaptive patterns in relation to water shortage—different solutions of the plant's problem of how to photosynthesize enough while also conserving water sufficiently to stay alive in a desert.

The two gradients of height and foliage persistence may now become the axes of a chart (Figure 2·7). They define a two-dimensional niche space or surface in which plant species have located themselves in evolution. The plant species are scattered in this space as the principle of Gause would lead us to expect: each species has its own distinctive niche area. Even though niche areas overlap, the centers of these areas are dispersed in the niche space. We have chosen only two niche gradients for this illustration, but there are many other niche characteristics that can be treated as gradients (along with some that are difficult to treat thus). For these many niche characteristics we may generalize our two-dimensional niche surface into an n-dimensional niche hyperspace. Each species occupies some part, or hypervolume, of the niche hyperspace, and the centers of these species hypervolumes are dispersed in the niche hyperspace.

The niche hyperspace concept, developed by G. E. Hutchinson, is most useful for interpreting the way the principle of Gause works out in practice among the species of a natural community. In particular it provides us with an approach to quantitative relations between the species we are interested in.

Let us assume first that there is some correspondence among three things—the fraction of the niche hyperspace of the community that a species occupies, the fraction of the community's resources (light, water, food, and so on) that the species utilizes, and the fraction of the community's productivity that that species realizes. Productivity

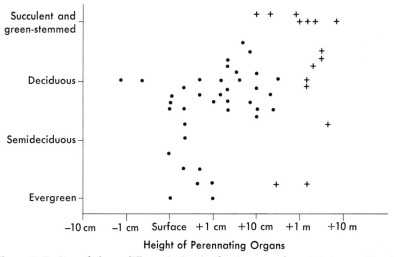

Figure 2·7. Growth-form differentiation in the Sonoran desert, Arizona. Woody plant species of the desert are plotted by the seasonal relations of their foliage, on the vertical axis, and plant height in relation to ground surface (on a logarithmic scale) on the horizontal axis. The larger woody plants of the community are armed with spines, as indicated by the crossed points. [Whittaker and Niering, 1965.]

(amount of organic matter produced) may serve as our approach to the species' importance. We must specify a measurement by which we shall compare species, and a number of these measurements or *impor-tance values* are possible. In dealing with a group of animals that are not too unlike in size of individuals we may use density (number of individuals per unit area) as an importance value. In dealing with plants, coverage (percentage of ground area covered by foliage) or some other measurement may be used to compare species. Productivity, however, is usually the preferred importance value if data are available, for it expresses the species' utilization of resources and permits com-parison of species of widely different sizes on a single scale. We may now ask how the niche space (and resources) of the community are divided, to produce what quantitative relations among productivities (or other importance values) of species.

A number of hypotheses have been suggested. We may treat these as multiple working hypotheses and use measurements of actual im-portance relations of species in communities to choose among them:

1. The random niche boundary hypothesis of MacArthur. One as-sumes that boundaries of niche hypervolumes of species are located at random positions in the hyperspace. It is much simpler to con-ceive of a one-dimensional "hyperspace," that is a line, onto which the points that represent niche boundaries are cast at random. We then break the line into segments separated by these points and arrange the segments, the lengths of which represent niche sizes, in order from the longest to the shortest. The segments form a curve from the longest segment (most important species) to the shortest segment (least important species); curve A in Figure 2·8 is of this form. (The lengths of the segments, and hence the importance values of species, should be distributed according to the series

$$I_r = \frac{N}{S} \sum_{i=1}^{r} \frac{1}{S-i+1}$$

In this, I_r is the importance value for a species, N is the total of importance values for all species in the community, S is the number of species in the community, and i is the number of the species in the sequence of species—from least important ($i = 1$), through the species in question ($i = r$), to the most important species ($i = S$). Σ indicates summation of values of $1/(S - i + 1)$ for the species from $i = 1$ to $i = r$.)

2. The niche pre-emption hypothesis. Suppose the sizes of niche hypervolumes are determined primarily by the success of certain species in pre-empting part of niche space, whereas less successful species occupy what is left. One most important species may occupy

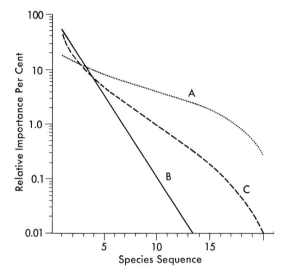

Figure 2·8. Three hypotheses on importance-value curves. The curves are all computed for a hypothetical sample of twenty species. **A:** Random niche boundary hypothesis. **B:** Geometric series, $c = 0.5$. **C:** Lognormal distribution. See Figure 2·10 for the manner in which the data are plotted. [Whittaker, 1965.]

a fraction k, say 50 per cent, of niche space, utilizing a corresponding fraction of community resources in a corresponding fraction of community productivity. This species is the dominant of the community. The second species is able to occupy a similar fraction of the niche space unoccupied by the first, and the third species a similar fraction of the niche space unoccupied by the first and second, and so on. The importance values of species will form a geometric series as suggested by Motomura,

$$I_n = Nk(1 - k)^{n-1} = Ac^{n-1}, k = 1 - c,$$

and when plotted in the manner of Figure 2·8 will form a straight line, curve B. (In the equations, n is the number of the species in the sequence from most to least important, c is the ratio of the importance value of a given species to that of its predecessor in the sequence, and A is the importance value of the most important species, the community dominant.)

3. The lognormal distribution of Preston. Extent of the niche space occupied by a species may be determined by a large number of factors affecting the relative success of one species in competition with other species in the hyperspace. If the relative importance of species populations is determined by a number of independent vari-

ables differently affecting different species, then a bell-shaped or normal distribution of importance values should result. If we again divide a line into segments with lengths representing importance values for species, we may group the segments by ranges of importance values to form a frequency distribution. A central or modal range of importance values will have the largest number of segments (i.e., species) in it, and smaller numbers of segments (species) will occur in importance-value ranges on each side of it. There will then be few very important species, and few very rare species, and many species of intermediate importance values in the community.

Figure 2·9 represents such a treatment—a frequency distribution of species by importance-value classes—from the same Sonoran desert as Figures 2·6 and 2·7. A bell-shaped normal curve has been fitted to the numbers of species in the ranges. The ranges, however, are related by units not of a linear but of a geometric scale; they are octaves whose limits are set by doubling of importance values from one octave to the next. The horizontal axis of the figure is consequently a logarithmic scale. A frequency distribution which becomes a symmetrical normal curve on a logarithmic scale is "lognormal"; our

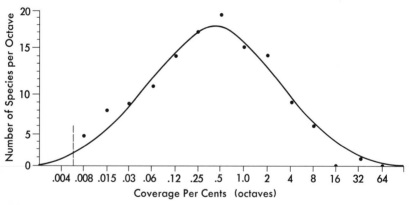

Figure 2·9. A lognormal distribution for plant species in the Sonoran desert, Arizona. Percentage of the ground surface covered by the foliage of a species is used as the importance value on the horizontal axis. The scale is logarithmic, with the species grouped by doubling units, or octaves, of coverage percentages. The largest numbers of species occur in the middle octaves of coverage of 0.12 to 2.0 per cent, and there are smaller numbers of species with very high or very low coverages. The dashed line on the left is a "veil line" below which no measurements are available. (The fitted curve is $s_r = 17.5 \, e^{-(0.245R)^2}$, where s_r is the number of species in an octave R octaves distant from the modal octave, which contains $s_0 = 17.5$ species.) [Whittaker, 1965.]

hypothesis on importance values of species is consequently that they form lognormal distributions.

The logarithmic scale is appropriate because the response of a population to environmental factors and combinations of factors is geometric, not linear. If the environment becomes more favorable, the population may increase not by a given number of individuals but by a given fraction of the population present at that time. Favorable environment might add 20 per cent to the population, say, hence 20 individuals to a population of 100 but 200 individuals to a population of 1,000. The effect of two factors on the populations is likely to be multiplicative rather than additive. Hence two factors that would each (with the other held constant) produce a doubling of the population may together produce effects approaching a fourfold increase. In comparing importance values of species in a community it is more appropriate to compare them by *ratios* of importance values—hence a logarithmic scale—than by absolute differences of importance values on a linear scale.

(Expressions of the lognormal distribution are

$$s_r = s_0 e^{-(aR)^2}, \quad \Sigma s_r = S = s_0 \sqrt{\pi}/a,$$

in which s_r is the number of species in an octave R octaves distant from the modal octave, which contains s_0 species, and a is a constant that often approximates 0.2.)

Figure 2·8 shows together the forms of the three curves applied to hypothetical communities. There are now many sets of data from communities that may be used to test the fit of the curves. The results are not quite what the proponents of any of the three hypotheses would have expected. Figure 2·10 illustrates some actual samples: (A) a small sample of nesting bird populations, which approaches the random niche boundary curve, (B) a high-elevation fir forest in the Great Smoky Mountains, which approaches the geometric series, and (C) a cove forest rich in species from the Great Smoky Mountains, which approaches lognormal distribution. Different samples from communities appear to fit all three models, together with intergradations among them. Instead of choosing among the three, we must ask when and why importance curves for species in communities approach one of the three models.

It appears that

1. The random niche boundary curve is approached by some small samples of taxonomically related animals from narrowly defined, homogeneous communities, for example, the nesting birds of a limited area in a forest. Fits are obtained only for some such samples, and primarily for higher animals with stable populations and relatively long life cycles. The random niche boundary hypoth-

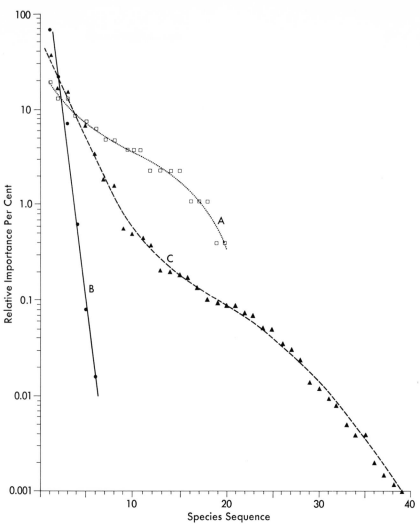

Figure 2·10. Three importance-value curves from natural communities. A: Nesting bird pairs (densities) in a deciduous forest, West Virginia; the data fit the random niche boundary hypothesis as shown in Figure 2·8A. **B:** Vascular plant species by net production in a subalpine fir forest in the Great Smoky Mountains, Tennessee. The data fit the geometric series and niche pre-emption hypothesis as shown in Figure 2·8B. **C:** Vascular plant species by net production in a deciduous cove forest in the Great Smoky Mountains of Tennessee, a community of much higher species-diversity. The data approach the lognormal distribution, as shown in Figure 2·8C and (in a different kind of plot) Figure 2·9. Each species is represented by a point located by that species' relative importance (the percentage that that species represents of the total net production, or total density, of all species in the community, on a logarithmic scale) on the vertical axis, and its position in the sequence of species from highest to lowest importance values, on the horizontal axis. Thus in curve B there are points for six species in a sequence of decreasing importance values, from the most important species at the top with 69 per cent, through other species with 23, 7.0, 0.62, and 0.08 per cent, to the least important species sampled, at the bottom with 0.016 per cent of net primary production for the forest.

esis thus describes a limiting case that some animal samples approach.

2. Some plant communities, especially those of severe environments and small numbers of species, approach geometric series. In such communities the phenomenon of dominance is strongly developed (in contrast to the animal groups just discussed, in which niche space is divided without strong dominance of any species). The resulting steep curves are an opposite limiting case from the rather flat random niche boundary curves.

3. In communities that are rich (in numbers of species), importance values in homogeneous samples approach lognormal curves. Such is the case with the cove forest (Figure 2·10) and in tropical rain forests, which are even richer. Samples that are not homogeneous, but combine species from a range of environments and communities (such as the collection of insects caught in a light trap), also approach lognormal distributions. The lognormal form may appear for a mixed sample even though the curves for individual communities (among those being combined) might approach the forms for either the random niche boundary hypothesis or the geometric series.

We may conclude that (a) a common theme—division of niche space with reduction of competition among species—underlies the varied forms of importance-value curves, but that (b) a variety of forms of importance-value curves, ranging from geometric through lognormal to random-boundary, appear when importance values are plotted for different groups of organisms and different communities, among these (c) samples including large numbers of species, whether from one community or combining related communities, will approach the lognormal. Students of the problem might have liked to find a single mathematical form for the relative importances of species in all communities. They may instead take satisfaction from the different expressions importance-value curves give to different manners of competition and niche division, different dominance and diversity structures in different communities.

Species-Diversity

The curves are related to another community characteristic of interest—relative richness in numbers of species. The fir forest and cove forest of Figure 2·10 grow in the same mountain range within a few kilometers of each other. The fir forest includes in a tenth of a hectare (20 × 50 m) 8 vascular plant species, the cove forests 46–68 species; they are in striking contrast in their richness in species or their *species-*

diversities.[1] The fir forest grows in cool climates of high elevations and the cove forests in warmer climates at lower elevations. We may judge from this pair (and support the judgment with other data) that species-diversities of plant communities increase toward lower elevations and warmer climates. We can extend the relation to the still warmer climates of the tropical rain forests, in which a sample may contain more than 100 species of trees, plus many other plant species. This trend of increasing species-diversities from the relatively poor communities of the high Arctic (and Alpine and Antarctic), toward the tropical rainforest and coral reef where profusion of species overwhelms the naturalist, is one of the major generalizations of biogeography.

It appears that few species are able to survive in the rigorous and widely fluctuating environments of the Arctic. A large share of the adaptation of these species must concern means of gaining the necessary food for growth and reproduction during the short favorable season. Evolution is affected more strongly by selection for survival in relation to problems of physical environment, less strongly by selection involving interaction and competition with other species. In the tropical rainforest the climate is warm and moist throughout the year and has been so for long periods of geological history. Very many species have been able to accommodate to a favorable and undemanding climate and to survive there. They can survive, however, only by solving the problems of competition with many other species also able to survive there—i.e., by niche differentiation. Their evolution is affected less strongly by selection for solution of problems of physical environment, more strongly by selection for success in solving, by more finely drawn and more varied niche differentiation, the problems of surviving

---

[1] Measurement of species-diversity: A number of measurements of species diversity have been used and can be experimented with by the student. The varied forms of importance-value curves make it necessary to distinguish two characteristics of these curves: (a) steepness of slope, or degree of concentration of dominance in one or a few species, and (b) richness of the community in numbers of species occurring in some unit or area. Steepness of slope tends to be inversely related to richness in species. It is quite possible, however, to have high species-diversity in communities of strong single-species dominance, and low species-diversity in communities of mixed dominance. Applications to vascular plant communities often measure slope and richness separately, applications to animal communities often use a single measurement combining the two. Most frequently used measurements are (a) steepness of slope, or concentration of dominance—the Simpson index, $c = \Sigma (I_n/N)^2$. The ratio c of the geometric series can also be used when appropriate. (For an alternative approach see Lloyd and Ghelardi, 1964, *J. Anim. Ecol.* **33**:217.) (b) Richness in species—counts of the numbers of species occurring in standard areas or samples of standard sizes. (For an alternative based on rate of increase in numbers of species with increase in sample size or area, $d = (S - 1)/\log N$.) (c) Combined richness and slope—the Shannon-Wiener information index, $d = -\Sigma (I_n/N)\log(I_n/N)$, Pielou, 1966, *J. Theoret. Biol.* **13**:131; Lloyd et al. 1968, *Amer. Midl. Nat* **79**:257. (An alternative now less frequently used is the alpha index of Fisher et al., 1943, *J. Anim. Ecol.* **12**:42.)

in relation to many other species in the same community. It is not assumed that this is the whole explanation of the diversity gradient in relation to latitude and altitude (which differently affects different groups of organisms and does not apply at all to some groups). The result, however, is a biogeographic gradient connecting contrasting extremes: (a) the tropical rainforests with their rich life, relatively stable populations, wealth of strikingly adapted forms, and occurrence of survivors of some ancient and primitive groups, versus (b) arctic communities with relatively poor and monotonous composition, more narrowly modern in the evolutionary relations of species, and with striking year-to-year fluctuations in some of their populations.

At a given latitude communities may differ widely in species diversity. Diversity of bird communities on land is strongly affected by stratal diversity, the complexity of vertical structure, of the vegetation. A grassland has a single major stratum of plants in which birds live, within which niche differences in food habits have evolved. Woodlands and forests have two or three strata of plants occupied by different groups of birds, and niche differentiation in food habits occurs within each of these groups. The woodlands and forests are richer in plant growth-forms (not necessarily in plant species) and in bird species. Among temperate-zone terrestrial plant communities, those of intermediate moisture conditions are usually richer in species than those of very wet or very dry environments. Among communities of intermediate moisture conditions, forests with closed canopies and limited development of undergrowth are less rich in plant species than woodlands with an open tree stratum and a highly developed undergrowth of shrubs and herbs. Among forests, those dominated by evergreen conifers are often less rich (because of less favorable soil and light conditions for undergrowth) than those dominated by deciduous trees. Study of vegetation structure makes possible reasonable predictions of the diversity of bird communities in different kinds of vegetation on continents. Predictions of richness of bird faunas of islands can be based on the size of the islands and their distance from other land. In other groups of organisms the relationships of species-diversities to kinds of environments and community structure have not yet been brought into effectively predictive treatment.

Summary

When we study the structure of natural communities we find them to be mixtures of plants and animals with different ways of life. Communities show vertical differentiation based on different plant growth-forms and animal species on different levels in the community. Communities show horizontal differentiation, expressed in the patchy or mosaiclike occurrence of species, and in correlations of species that tend to occur together, or to occur separately in relation to the patches. Communities show temporal differentiation, with different species carrying on similar functions at different times in seasonal and daily cycles. Each species has its own place in vertical and horizontal space, time, and way of relating to other species in a given community; the species' place in the community in relation to other species is its niche. Species evolve toward difference in niche, by which competition between them is reduced. In general no two species will occupy the same niche, utilizing the same resources at the same time and place, in the same stable community.

The gradients of niche characteristics by which species of the community can be compared may be treated as axes of an abstract niche space, or hyperspace. Species evolve toward dispersion of their adaptive centers in the hyperspace. Species differ widely in relative importance in the community. We may conceive importance as dependent on the fraction of niche space the species occupies and the fraction of community resources it utilizes, and measure importance as the species' fraction of the productivity (or other dimension) for the community as a whole. Importance values for species in a community may be arranged in progressions from most to least important species. These progressions are of at least three intergrading forms that can be interpreted by three different hypotheses on niche hyperspace division and determination of relative importance—random niche boundaries, niche pre-emption and the geometric series, and the lognormal distribution. Communities differ also in species-diversity, or richness in numbers of species. Species-diversities show a broad trend of increase from arctic, antarctic, and alpine environments into the tropics, and marked correlations with vegetation structure or physiognomy, and other relationships yet to be clarified. A community is a functional system of interacting, niche-differentiated species; and community structure, differentiation in space and time, importance-value progressions, and species-diversities are interrelated expressions of the interaction and organization of species in communities.

References

Allee, W. C., O. Park, A. E. Emerson, T. Park, and K. P. Schmidt. (1949) *Principles of Animal Ecology.* Philadelphia and London: Saunders. xii + 837 pp. (especially Chapters 22, 26, 28).

Boughey, Arthur S. (1968) *Ecology of Populations.* New York: Macmillan. viii + 135 pp.

Braun-Blanquet, J. (1932) *Plant Sociology.* (Trans. by G. D. Fuller and H. S. Conard.) New York: McGraw-Hill. xviii + 439 pp.

Cox, George W. (1967) *Laboratory Manual of General Ecology.* Dubuque: Brown. ix + 165 pp.

Dansereau, Pierre. (1957) *Biogeography: An Ecological Perspective.* New York: Ronald. xiii + 394 pp.

Elton, Charles. (1947) *Animal Ecology,* 2nd ed. London: Sidgwick & Jackson. xx + 209 pp.

Gause, G. F. (1934) *The Struggle for Existence.* Reprint, 1964, New York and London: Hafner. ix + 163 pp.

Greig-Smith, P. (1964) *Quantitative Plant Ecology,* 2nd ed. Butterworths: London. xii + 256 pp.

Hazen, William E., editor. (1964) *Readings in Population and Community Ecology.* Philadelphia and London: Saunders. x + 388 pp.

Hutchinson, G. E. (1965) *The Ecological Theater and the Evolutionary Play.* New Haven and London: Yale University. xiii + 139 pp.

Slobodkin, Lawrence B. (1962) *Growth and Regulation of Animal Populations.* New York: Holt, Rinehart, and Winston. viii + 184 pp.

Smith, Robert Leo. (1966) *Ecology and Field Biology.* New York and London: Harper & Row. xiv + 686 pp.

Cole, L. C. (1949) "The measurement of interspecific association." *Ecology,* **30:**411–424.

Hardin, G. (1960) "The competitive exclusion principle." *Science,* **131:** 1292–1297.

Hutchinson, G. E. (1958) "Concluding remarks." *Cold Spring Harbor Symposia on Quantitative Biology,* **22:**415–427.

Hutchinson, G. E. (1959) "Homage to Santa Rosalia, *or* why are there so many kinds of animals?" *American Naturalist,* **93:**145–159.

MacArthur, R. H. (1965) "Patterns of species diversity." *Biological Reviews,* **40:**510–533.

MacArthur, R. H. and J. W. MacArthur. (1961) "On bird species diversity." *Ecology,* **42:**594–598.

MacArthur, R. H., and E. O. Wilson. (1963) "An equilibrium theory of insular zoogeography." *Evolution,* **17:**373–387.

Margalef, R. (1967) "Some comments relative to the organization of plankton." *Oceanography and Marine Biology, an Annual Review,* **5:**257–289.

Paine, R. T. (1966) "Food web complexity and species diversity." *American Naturalist,* **100:**65–76.

Pianka, E. R. (1966) "Latitudinal gradients in species diversity: a review of concepts." *American Naturalist,* **100:**33–46.

Preston, F. W. (1948) "The commonness, and rarity, of species." *Ecology,* **29:**254–283.

Sanders, H. L. (1968) "Marine benthic diversity: a comparative study." *American Naturalist,* **102:**243–282.

Whittaker, R. H. (1965) "Dominance and diversity in land plant communities." *Science,* **147:**250–260.

Communities and Environments

Species Along Environmental Gradients

ONE TRAVELS TOWARD the mountains across the lowlands, somewhere west of the Rocky Mountains, through miles of semidesert scrub. The sagebrush scrub extends up onto lower foothills, but as one climbs scattered small junipers appear. Somewhat higher in the mountains, larger and more numerous junipers are joined by piñon pines to form an open woodland of small trees with an undergrowth of grasses and shrubs. As one climbs further the woodland is denser, and scattered large trees of western yellow or ponderosa pine appear; then the piñon and juniper decrease in numbers while the pines increase until one climbs through a forest of ponderosa pines. Still higher these pines give way to forests of Douglas fir and white fir; still higher these in turn give way to forests of Engelmann spruce and alpine fir. One climbs now through the uppermost forests of the mountain, until the trees become small and scattered or reduced to shrubby patches in meadows. Beyond this forest edge are the alpine meadows of the high country. The meadows extend upward, but become sparser toward higher altitudes, and finally are reduced to lichens and a few herbs among the rocks of the mountain summit.

Changes of vegetation with altitude in mountains are observed throughout the world; description of these changes in the form of "life-zones" by C. H. Merriam was one of the early developments in ecology. In Merriam's treatment the vegetation forms a series of zones in relation to temperature gradients, each zone being characterized by major plant and animal species. We are observing, however, a phenomenon broader than elevation zones—the response of species populations and

34

communities to environmental gradients. We need therefore to ask more general questions than Merriam's:

1. How are species populations distributed in relation to one another and communities along an environmental gradient?
2. How are kinds of communities in an area related to patterns of more than one environmental gradient?
3. How are we to interpret world-wide relations of communities to climatic gradients?

Consider first a single environmental gradient, which could be a long, even, uninterrupted slope of a mountain. The slope is occupied by many species of plants, animals, and saprobes. We have seen that these species have evolved in relation to one another, that they influence one another's populations, that some are competing, and that these will have evolved in such ways that competition is reduced by niche differentiation. What kind of distributional relations between species along the gradient will result from this evolution? We may consider four hypotheses before turning to evidence from the field for decision:

1. Competing species, including dominant plants, exclude one another along sharp boundaries. Other species evolve toward close association with the dominants and toward adaptation for living with one another. There thus develop distinct zones along the gradient, each zone having its own assemblage of species adapted to one another, and giving way at a sharp boundary to another assemblage of species adapted to one another (Figure 3·1A).
2. Competing species exclude one another along sharp boundaries, but do not become organized into groups with parallel distributions (Figure 3·1B).
3. Competition does not, for the most part, result in sharp boundaries between species populations. Evolution of species toward adaptation to one another will, however, result in the appearance of groups of species with similar distributions (Figure 3·1C).
4. Competition does not usually produce sharp boundaries between species populations, and evolution of species in relation to one another does not produce well-defined groups of species with similar distributions. Centers and boundaries of species populations are scattered along the environmental gradient (Figure 3·1D).

To test these possibilities the mountain vegetation described in the introduction to this chapter can be studied. Vegetation samples, with

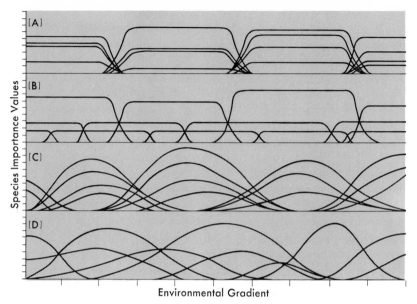

Figure 3·1. Four hypotheses on how species populations might relate to one another along an environmental gradient. Each curve in each part of the figure represents one species population and the way it might be distributed along the environmental gradient.

suitable measurements of importances of plant populations, are taken along the elevation gradient from the tops of the mountains down to the bases. To study the distributions of populations effectively we should (a) have samples from comparable environments—open, south-facing slopes, say—for all elevations, and (b) have a large enough number of samples so that they can be grouped and averaged at elevation intervals. We may want, say, to average five or more samples for every 100 m. elevation change to smooth out irregularities in population distribution. The result is a *transect* with tables showing the way each species population is distributed in relation to the elevation gradient, other species, and the kinds of communities we have observed. We can do the same along the topographic moisture gradient. This is the gradient of soil moisture and atmospheric humidity from moist canyon bottoms through environments that are increasingly dry —lower slopes of the canyon, open, north-facing slopes, intermediate (east- and west-facing) slopes to the driest open, south- and southwest-facing slopes. For this transect elevation should be held constant, and the samples should be averaged for different positions along the moisture gradient.

When we thus study the manner in which plant populations rise and fall along environmental gradients, the results support hypothesis 4

(Figure 3·1D, and Figure 3·2). (Cases of sharp boundaries between competing species and of close distributional association of species are known, but populations are usually distributed as in Figure 3·2).

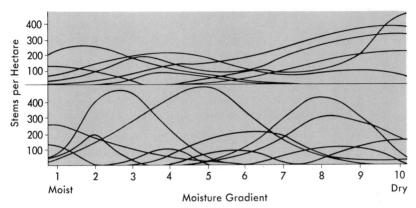

Figure 3·2. Actual distributions of species populations along environmental gradients. Species populations are plotted by densities, numbers of tree stems 2 cm or more in diameter per hectare (10^4 m²) on the vertical scale, in samples taken along a topographic moisture gradient from moist environments of ravines to dry environments of southwest-facing slopes, on the horizontal axis. The data are from the Siskiyou Mountains, Oregon, 760–1,070 m elevation, above, and the Santa Catalina Mountains, Arizona, 1,830–2,140 m elevation, below. [Whittaker, 1967.]

Observations agree with the "principle of species individuality" asserted by Gleason and Ramensky before recent field studies of the problem:

1. Each species is distributed in its own way, according to its own genetic, physiological, and life-cycle characteristics and its way of relating to both physical environment and interactions with other species; hence no two species are alike in distribution.
2. The broad overlap and scattered centers of species populations along a gradient imply that most communities intergrade continuously along environmental gradients, rather than forming distinct, clearly separated zones. (Either environmental discontinuity or disturbance by fire, logging, and so on, can of course produce discontinuities between communities.)

It is useful to recognize life-zones, as Merriam did, as major kinds of communities in relation to temperature. But the zones are continuous with one another: distributions of the major plant species by which we recognize the zones overlap broadly, and other plants and animals do not form groups with distributions closely similar to those of the dominants. The zones are kinds of communities man recognizes, mainly by their dominant plants, within the continuous change of plant populations and communities along the elevation gradient. The zones may be compared to the colors man recognizes, and accepts as useful concepts, within the spectrum of wave lengths of light, which are known to be continuous.

It is of interest to ask *why* species do not evolve to form groups with parallel distributions. We have shown in Figure 2·5 how two species that come into competition in relation to a niche gradient tend to diverge: selection increases the difference between the mean adaptive positions of the two species populations along the niche gradient. For niche gradient, now, we may substitute habitat gradient as the horizontal axis of Figure 2·5. The two species are in close competition (in the same or closely related niches) within the same range of an environmental or habitat gradient, such as elevation or topographic moisture. Selection will increase the difference in mean adaptive positions along the habitat gradient. As competing species evolve toward difference of niche, so they evolve also toward difference of habitat.

In a simplified case of this process, a number of species occur along an environmental gradient (Figure 3·3). A new species, number 4, enters the area. Its potential distribution along the gradient (on the basis of genetic characteristics evolved in another area) is indicated by

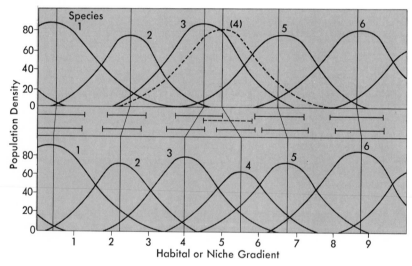

Figure 3·3. Establishment of a new species along a community gradient. The new species, number 4, has a potential distribution along the habitat gradient as represented in the dashed line of the upper figure. In competition with species 3 and 5 it fits in between these, as indicated in the lower figure. The bars between the figures represent dispersions, the degrees of deviation or spread of the populations on each side of their mean positions along the gradient.

the broken line in the upper part of the figure. Because species 4 is strongly in competition with species 3, however, its population shifts position toward 5 and occupies a position between the other two species, in the lower part of the figure. Compensating shifts occur in distributions of other species, and widths of their distributions along the gradient, indicated by the bars between the figures, are reduced. Species 4 survives and takes its own position along the gradient by virtue of both a sufficient niche differentiation from species 3 and 5 to survive in their presence, and a new range of habitat preference that reduces the competition, which does result from partial niche overlap.

Evolution of populations in directions that reduce competition thus leads both toward niche differentiation and toward habitat differentiation and the scattering of population centers along environmental gradients. Selection toward a distinctive niche and a distinctive habitat preference will normally occur at the same time, for niche and habitat are closely related aspects of the species' total adaptation to environment. Many widespread species include a number of subpopulations (subspecies or ecotypes) showing marked differences in habitat adaptation, and sometimes differences in niche also. So far as the plant populations along a given environmental gradient are concerned, however, the consequences of selection lead primarily away from, not toward, formation of groups of species with parallel distributions.

Figure 3·2 illustrates a further expression of this evolutionary process. The two community gradients shown occur along similar environmental gradients (the topographic moisture gradient from canyons to south-facing slopes of the same elevations in mountains). Individual samples of the forests in the two areas are of similar species diversity. Yet the number of species encountered along the gradient in the figure below is higher, for the species' distributions are narrower. There is a more extensive floristic turnover of species replacing one another along the gradient. We may thus distinguish *alpha* diversity, in the sense of richness in species of particular community samples, and *beta* diversity, or the degree of change in species composition of communities along a gradient. The lower transect of Figure 3·2 has conspicuously higher beta diversity.

We can approach measurement of beta diversity through degree of change in composition of samples along the gradient, or extent of difference in samples from opposite ends of the gradient. There are a number of ways of measuring relative similarity of samples from communities. (The two simplest are: Coefficient of community, $CC = S_{ab}/(S_a + S_b - S_{ab})$. The coefficient of community is the ratio of the number of species shared by samples A and B (S_{ab}) to the total number of species occurring in sample A (S_a), or sample B (S_b), or both. Percentage similarity, $PS = 1 - 0.5 \Sigma|a - b| = \Sigma \min(a,b)$, or $PS' = 1$

$-\sqrt{\Sigma (a-b)^2}$. For each species, a and b are that species' percentage of the total for a given importance value in samples A and B respectively. Percentage similarity is based on the sum of the signless differences between the a and b values for each species and expresses the degree to which the samples are alike in quantitative representation of species. It may also be computed by summing the smaller of the percentages in the two samples for all species, Σ min (a,b), or as the different but closely related measurement PS'.) These measurements (or their complements) express *ecological distance*—the degree to which samples differ from one another in species composition because of their separation along environmental gradients, or other factors. The higher beta diversity of the lower community gradient of Figure $3 \cdot 2$ is expressed in lower percentage similarities of the samples at the extremes of the gradients (0.9 per cent versus 18 per cent), hence greater ecological distance between them. It can also be expressed by *half-change* values for turnovers of species composition along the gradients: these values are 1.4 for the lower beta diversity of the upper transect, 3.4 for the higher beta diversity of the lower transect.

Alpha and beta diversity will be recognized as consequences of niche diversification and habitat diversification of species, respectively. The two aspects of diversity may vary in parallel along some climatic gradients; both increase from the coastal redwood belt inland in the area of mountains from which the upper transect of Figure $3 \cdot 2$ was taken. In studying bird communities along the diversity gradient from cold climates into the tropics MacArthur found the two somewhat independent. Alpha diversity for birds, which is closely related to vegetation structure, was similar in temperate and tropical communities of similar structure. Beta diversity, however, increased into the tropics. It appears that there is a point of saturation, or maximum feasible division of niches among bird species for a given vegetation structure. Evolution in the tropics acts not to increase alpha diversity beyond this saturation but to fit additional species in along environmental gradients by habitat differentiation and narrowed habitat distributions—it acts to increase beta diversity.

Community Patterns

We have been discussing population structure of communities along environmental gradients. Three concepts are implicit in this treatment. First, there is the concept of *community gradient* (*coenocline*), represented in terms of populations in Figure $3 \cdot 2$. Second, there is the conception of environmental gradients, which usually involve many environmental factors that change through space together. Thus the "elevation gradient" includes decreasing mean temperatures, decreasing lengths of growing seasons, increasing rainfall, increasing wind speeds, and so on, toward higher elevations. All these factors act together on plants and animals, and it may be difficult without experiment to judge what factors are most important for a given population. The assemblage of environmental factors that change together through the space along which a community gradient occurs and that influence its populations may be termed a *complex-gradient*. Third, the complex-gradient and coenocline together are a gradient of communities-and-environments, or a gradient of ecosystems, an *ecocline*.

The approach to communities through ecoclines is important because it permits us to study the way gradients of species populations and community characteristics change in response to, or in concurrence with, gradients of environment. Research approaches that relate gradients to one another on these three levels—environmental factors, species populations, and community characteristics—are termed *gradient analysis* and are the major alternative to approaches to communities through classification. (In the latter, types of communities are recognized, and these community types may then be characterized in terms of environmental measurements, species composition, and other community characteristics.) In many cases it is appropriate to combine the approaches of classification and gradient analysis in a given study. The preceding section dealt with results from gradient analysis applied to questions of how species populations relate to one another and communities along particular environmental gradients. We need also to consider applications of gradient analysis to patterns of communities in relation to more than one environmental gradient.

In mountains, for example, both elevation and topographic moisture have great effects on communities, and both should be studied together. It is quite possible to use transects both of elevation and of topographic moisture to study mountain vegetation. The two kinds of transects cross one another to form a grid covering the vegetation pattern by which the pattern may be analyzed. For some purposes, however, a different approach to a pattern of mountain communities is more effective. The two kinds of complex-gradients may be used as vertical and horizontal axes of a chart as in Figure 3·4. Vegetation samples taken essentially at random from many positions on the mountain topography can be located at points in relation to these axes, and at each of these points importance values for species and classification of the sample into a community type can be entered. Species populations and community types can then be outlined on the chart to show their relations to one another and to mountain environments.

Figure 3·4 shows relations of vegetation types to elevation and topographic moisture in the Santa Catalina Mountains of southeastern

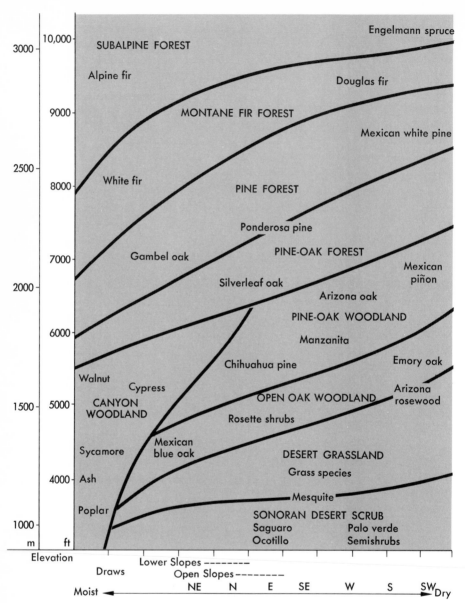

Figure 3·4. A vegetation chart for the Santa Catalina Mountains, southeastern Arizona. (The pattern above 9,000 feet is for the nearby Pinaleño Mountains.) Four hundred vegetation samples were plotted on the chart by their positions in relation to the elevation gradient, on the left, and the topographic moisture gradient, on the bottom. Boundary lines were drawn to connect the mean positions at which one community type, as these had been defined in this study, gave way to another. Dominant species are indicated in the parts of the pattern where they are most important. [Whittaker and Niering, 1965.]

Arizona, a mountain range with strong Mexican influence. These points of interest may be observed from the chart:

1. The pattern is dominated by effects of increasing aridity toward lower elevations. Apart from the canyon forests this pattern (though not those of some more humid mountains) forms a series of zones in response to moisture conditions related to elevation. At a given elevation north-facing slopes and canyons are cooler and more humid, south-facing slopes warmer and more arid. The zones are consequently tilted: a given zone occurs at higher elevations on south slopes than on north slopes and in canyons.

2. The zones are defined by growth-forms and dominant species. A sequence of growth-forms replace one another as community dominants in a continuous, flowing fashion; from high elevations to low these are needle-leaved trees, sclerophyll trees (evergreen oaks), small needle-leaved trees (juniper and piñon), together with evergreen-sclerophyll and rosette shrubs, grasses, and the spinose shrubs and the semishrubs of the desert.

3. A species population has a bell-shaped distribution along each environmental gradient. Its population distribution in relation to two gradients may be conceived as a bell-shaped or hill-shaped solid (Figure 3·5). Different ecotypes in the species may be indicated by separate peaks, with different central points of adaptation. In two dimensions as in one, species populations overlap broadly, and the locations of their population centers are scattered in the pattern. Because a community pattern like that of Figure 3·4 includes hundreds of vascular plant species, it may be conceived as a complex population continuum formed by these many, overlapping species populations.

4. Community and soil characteristics too show patterns in relation to the pattern of environments. Species-diversity increases from high elevations to low, hence from moist forests to the desert of lower mountain slopes in this area. The amount of organic matter produced, on the other hand, in this area decreases from high elevations to low in response to the moisture gradient. Soil pH and nutrient content increase, soil organic matter content decreases, from high elevations to low.

5. The chart thus permits us to represent many of the relationships of environmental factors, species populations, and communities to one another; it makes possible a conception of the vegetation as a pattern of populations and communities corresponding to a pattern of environments.

In many areas three or more environmental gradients have signifi-

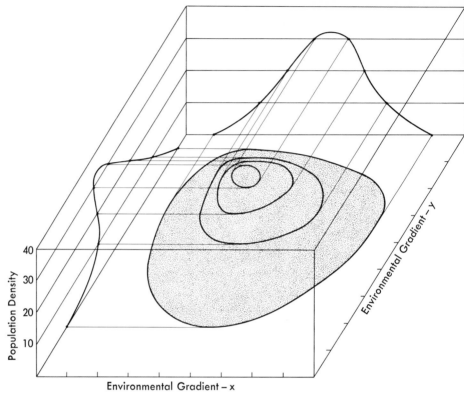

Figure 3·5. Population solid for a species in relation to two environmental gradients. The distribution forms a bell-shaped or hill-shaped figure, with population density decreasing in all directions away from the population center or peak. In any transect of communities along a single environmental gradient that cuts through this population solid, a bell-shaped curve of population density will be obtained.

cant effects on communities. Various kinds of soil factors and disturbance factors are often to be considered, and it may not be appropriate to base the study on assumptions about which of these are most important. In this case it is possible to approach the recognition of major environmental gradients indirectly, causing them to emerge from an analysis of community samples, rather than accepting them in advance as was done in the study just described.

A set of samples are taken to represent a range of communities to be investigated. These samples are compared with one another in all possible combinations by coefficient of community, or percentage similarity, or other related measurements. A table results that contains similarity measurements for each sample compared with every other sample. Some of the samples, however, are marginal to the set as a whole, as indicated by the fact that the sums of their similarities to other samples are particularly low. Two samples that are marginal in this sense, and that are least similar to one another, can be chosen as a first pair of end points for an axis. Each of the other samples in the set may now be compared with these end point samples and may be located, somewhere along the axis between them, by relative similarity to the two end points. All the samples of the set may be thus arranged (ordinated) along the axis.

Among the samples near the middle of the axis, some may be quite dissimilar. The pair of these that are least similar may be chosen as end points for a second axis, and all other samples may be arranged along this axis also. The process can be carried on to a third axis, and if necessary a fourth. The product is an arrangement, or ordination, of the samples in an abstract space defined by the axes. The samples are being treated in terms of a hyperspace of axes that are not niche gradients, but gradients of change in the species composition of samples. These gradients presumably correspond to ecoclines, but they are not yet identified as such.

Figure 3·6 illustrates such an arrangement in a simple case, limited to two dimensions and ten samples representing different types of communities. The ten types are from a forested landscape in Poland; they range from wet ash-alder woods (carr) and bog with scattered pines to dry pine-bilberry forest and hazelnut brush. With the samples arranged in the chart, values for environmental variables can be plotted at the points for samples. It is then apparent that soil moisture decreases from upper left to lower right across the pattern, whereas soil fertility increases from lower left to upper right. The arrangement thus represents a pattern of communities in relation to a pattern of soil characteristics. The axes are in fact ecoclines, but their direction in the pattern is oblique in relation to the conventional gradients of soil moisture and soil fertility. It is usually possible to interpret such a pattern in terms of known environmental factors. In some cases axes represent effects of environmental variables that had not been recognized before the sample arrangement was prepared and studied. The axes are in some cases gradients of disturbance effects, or of community development, rather than of stable communities in relation to habitat gradients.

Community characteristics form gradients through the pattern also. Diversities (numbers of plant species in samples) increase, as illustrated, along the fertility gradient (but are lower in the dry hazelnut brush). In the central place in the pattern are the fir forests, which grow in habitats intermediate for the area—neither especially wet, nor dry, nor of especially low fertility, nor on soils rich in lime. For the uplands of the area the fir forests form the largest part of the vegetation pattern where it is not disturbed by man; they are a prevailing community type for the landscape. It may be observed that at a given elevation one type

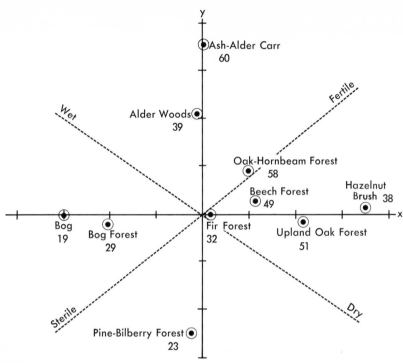

Figure 3·6. An arrangement of ten communities from an area of forests in Poland in relation to two axes. Each sample is an average of a number of field samples representing a community type (data of Frydman, *Ecology,* **49:896, 1968).** The bog and hazelnut brush served as end-point samples for the first, x, axis; pine bilberry forest and ash-alder carr for the second, y, axis. Samples were located by relative similarity (coefficients of community) to these end-point samples; units of ecological distance marked on the axes are 10 per cent coefficient of community. The dashed lines are gradients of soil characteristics that are oblique in relation to the axes; the numbers are mean numbers of plant species in the field samples.

of community may prevail in the vegetation of Figure 3·4 also; at 8,000 feet, for example, pine forests are most extensive but fir forests occur in moist, pine-oak forests in dry habitats. The undisturbed community that is most extensive in the vegetation of a given area, or elevation belt, may be thought to express most effectively the climate of that area. The treatment of community types in relation to climates that follows is consequently based on relating the most extensive, or prevalent, communities to climatic gradients.

As samples can be arranged in patterns, so can species. Correlations, which express relative similarity of occurrence in samples, can be computed for every species of a set of samples compared with every other species. The correlation values may then be used to arrange the species in a hyperspace that is related to, though not the same as, that derived from similarity comparisons and arrangement of samples. Statistical techniques of factor analysis may be used for this purpose, rather than the simpler approach through end points of axes. Species appear in most cases to have scattered positions when they are arranged in a hyperspace. In general the approaches described—treatment in terms of recognized environmental gradients, arrangement based on quantitative comparison of samples, and on correlation analysis of species distributions—give convergent results in the study of community patterns.

Major Ecoclines

The concepts of ecocline, community type, and pattern may serve well to relate communities to climate on a world-wide scale. Four ecoclines on land are to be described; but the principles apply to aquatic and shore communities, and a gradient of shore communities will be described first.

1. Rocky ocean shores, intertidal levels. A complex rhythm of rising and falling tides alternately submerges shore communities in sea water and exposes them to the air, and from low to high tide levels a gradient of increasing exposure to drying (and other environmental fluctuation) affects organisms. At low tide levels there occurs a dense and rich community of many species of algae and marine animals that are only briefly exposed. Some of these species extend upward into a lower mid-tidal belt of varied algae and certain animals (sea anemones, sea urchins, starfish, oysters, and so on) tolerant of longer, but limited exposure to the air. Although some of these organisms occur also in upper mid-tidal levels, communities of the latter are dominated by animals more distinctly adapted to longer exposure—notably mussels, barnacles, and limpets. Of these the barnacles extend farthest upward, and the upper edge of the barnacle community merges into an upper tidal belt in which snails adapted to prolonged exposure are the most abundant animals, although crusts of blue-green algae and lichens occupy rock surfaces. Organisms of this meager community become increasingly sparse upward, through supratidal levels never submerged but affected by wave splash and salt spray, to rock surfaces that receive salt spray but are occupied by plants and animals of terrestrial derivation.

2. Climatic moisture gradient, southern United States—Appalachian forest to Sonoran desert (Figure 3·7A). Westward from the Southern Appalachians rich mixed, broad-leaved deciduous forests of humid climates in the mountains change in character until more

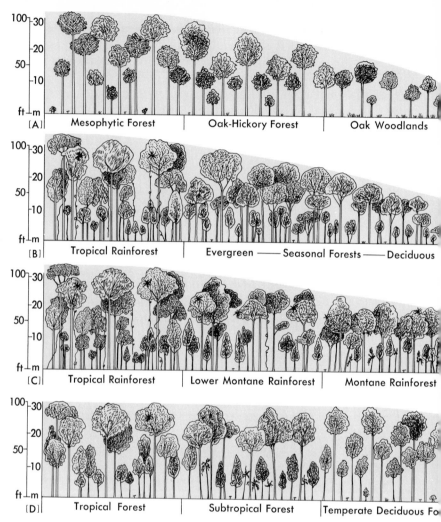

Figure 3·7. Profile diagrams for four ecoclines. A: Along a gradient of increasing aridity from mesophytic (moist) forest in the Appalachian Mountains westward to desert in the southern United States. **B:** Along a gradient of increasing aridity from rainforest to desert in South America. **C:** Along an elevation gradient up tropical mountains in South America from tropical rainforest to paramo or alpine meadow. **D:** Along a temperature gradient from tropical seasonal forest northward in forest climates to the arctic tundra. [**B** and **C** are modified from Beard, 1955.]

open oak-hickory forests are encountered. Stature and density of these decrease until oak woodlands (or in many areas a sharp forest edge produced by fire) give way to prairie. Height of the prairie grasses decreases westward from tall-grass prairie to the short-grass plains below the Rocky Mountains and the desert grass-

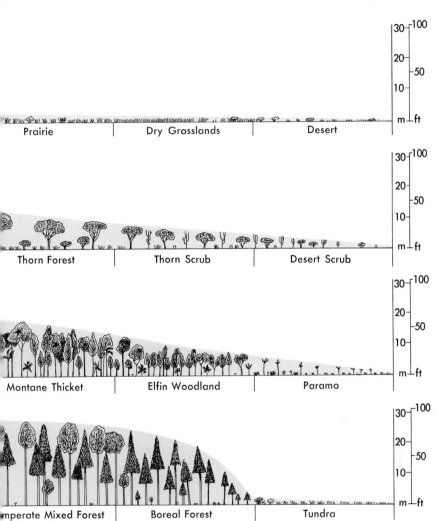

lands west of the Rockies in New Mexico. The dry grasslands give way to creosote bush desert in southern Arizona (or, farther north to sagebrush semidesert). Height and coverage of the desert shrubs decreases toward the still more arid desert climates of southwestern Arizona.

3. Climatic moisture gradient in tropical South America (Figure 3·7B). Tropical rainforests of large, evergreen, broad-leaved trees change into seasonal forests toward drier climates with rainfall deficient during part of the year. Toward drier climates in the seasonal forests the trees are smaller and the canopy more open, and the proportion of evergreen trees decreases while that of deciduous

trees increases. The deciduous seasonal forests give way to thorn forests, usually of more open structure with grass undergrowth, and from these size of trees decreases into denser, lower thorn scrub with spinose shrubs and cacti. The thorn scrub in turn becomes a more open desert scrub, and in still drier climates the desert scrub becomes a desert of sparse plant coverage.

4. A temperature gradient upward in tropical mountains (Figure 3·7C). The tropical rainforests decrease in stature of trees from the base of the mountains through the lower montane and montane rainforest as one climbs. The montane rainforest (or cloud forest) is essentially a temperate rainforest of cooler, but very humid, climates within tropical latitudes. Sizes of trees decrease further into a dense montane thicket, with rosette trees and many epiphytes, and beyond this into an impenetrable elfin woodland of small trees and shrubs, densely crusted with lichens and mosses. Elfin woodland of decreasing height and coverage gives way finally to the treeless alpine meadow or paramo of South America, with grasses and distinctive rosette shrubs of the sunflower family.

5. Temperature gradient from the tropics northward in forest climates (Figure 3·7D). Tropical semievergreen forests dominated by broad-leaved trees, some of them deciduous, smaller than the rainforest trees and with fewer epiphytes, change northward through less rich subtropical forests and transitional semideciduous forests to temperate broad-leaved forests. (This sequence may be followed from Venezuela along the Caribbean Islands to Florida and the southern Appalachian Mountains.) Warm-temperate forests of a continental climate, dominated by broad-leaved deciduous trees, occur in the southern Appalachians and were used for the beginning of ecocline 2. Northward these give way to other temperate deciduous forests less rich in species, and these (in the area of the Great Lakes) to forests of deciduous trees mixed with needle-leaved evergreen trees. Still farther northward evergreen trees (spruces and firs) are dominant in boreal forests (taiga) similar to those of the upper forest zone described at the beginning of the chapter. As in the mountains, the forest opens out into treeless vegetation; in the Far North this is the arctic plain or tundra which extends northward to the lands bordering the Arctic Ocean.

There are some conclusions to be drawn from such ecoclines:

1. Along a gradient from a "favorable" environment to an "extreme" environment there is normally a decrease in the productivity and massiveness of communities. The decrease in amount of organic matter per unit area is expressed in decrease of height of dominant

organisms and percentage of the ground surface covered. Thus on land a climatic ecocline may lead from a high forest with a dry weight biomass exceeding 40 kg/m², canopy tree height of 40 m, and coverage (counting overlap of different strata of trees, shrubs, and herbs) well above 100 per cent, to a desert with a biomass less than 1 kg/m², plant height below 1 m, and plant coverage less than 10 per cent.

2. Related to these are gradients in physiognomic complexity. Toward increasingly unfavorable environments there is a stepping-down of community structure and a reduction of stratal differentiation, with generally smaller numbers of growth-forms arranged in fewer and lower strata.

3. Trends in diversity of structure are broadly paralleled by those in diversity of species. In general (but with exceptions as regards both particular ecoclines and particular groups of organisms), alpha and beta species-diversities decrease from favorable to extreme environments, whether the latter are extremes of drought, or of cold, or of adverse soil chemistry, or (for the sea coast) of tidal exposure.

4. Each growth-form has its characteristic place of maximum importance along the ecoclines—rosette trees in some tropical forests, semishrubs in desert and adjacent semiarid communities, and so on. (Some growth-forms, for example, grasses and grasslike plants, may have more than one area of importance along the major ecoclines.) A growth-form, like a species, has dual aspects of adaptation to niche and habitat. Growth-forms are both broad niche categories among plants and broadly significant expressions of plant adaptation to physical environment.

5. The last observation implies that the same growth-forms may be dominant in similar environments in widely different parts of the world. Because of this fact, along with the relationships in points 1 and 2, similar environments on different continents tend to have communities of similar physiognomy. This adaptive convergence at the level of the community is one of the major generalizations about the geography of life.

Biome-Types

For further discussion it is helpful to change perspective from emphasis on continuities to classification. A major kind of community, conceived in terms of physiognomy, on a given continent is a *biome* or *formation*. (*Formation* is used when the concern is with plant communities only, *biome* when the concern is with both plants and animals. These units may be the same, but biomes defined with vertebrate animals in mind are in some cases broader units than formations.) Thus the elfin woodlands of tropical Central and South America are a biome, and the broad-leaved deciduous forests of the temperate eastern United States are a biome. Because some growth-forms are dominant in a number of different major environments, we have to use both structure and environment when we define biomes. Thus alpine sedge meadow and temperate prairie, saltmarsh and paramo of tropical mountains are different biomes, though all are dominated by grasses or grasslike plants. A biome is a grouping of terrestrial ecosystems on a given continent that are similar in vegetation structure or physiognomy, in the major features of environment to which this structure is a response, and in some characteristics of their animal communities. The biome concept is most widely applied to land ecosystems but can also be applied in aquatic environments—to such zones as the world-wide structural types defined by major kinds of organisms in rocky-shore ecoclines, for example.

Similar deciduous forests of temperate continental climates occur in North America and Eurasia. Elfin woodlands occur in widely separated areas in Africa, South America, and New Guinea. The still broader grouping of convergent biomes or formations of different continents is a *biome-type* or *formation-type*. Biome-types or formation-types are the best way to describe major kinds of communities on a world-wide scale. The outline of formation-types that follows is limited to major communities and is very brief in its statement on each of these. Further treatments may be found in books in the reference list and other books on plant geography. For a number of reasons, outlines of types differ from one author to another.

(1) Tropical rainforests occur in the humid tropics where rainfall is abundant and well distributed through the year, in South and Central America, Africa, Southeast Asia, the East Indies, and northeast Australia. Trees are often tall, of numerous species, some with buttressed bases, and mostly have medium-sized, evergreen leaves. Tree-ferns are often present, large woody climbers or lianas extend from the forest floor to the canopy, and the canopy is adorned with numerous epiphytic orchids and bromeliads. The invertebrate animal life is exceedingly rich, vertebrate animal life is rich but not conspicuously so beyond the temperate zone; a high proportion of the mammals are arboreal.

(2) Tropical seasonal forests, including monsoon forests and other deciduous and semideciduous forests, occur in humid tropical climates with a pronounced dry season, during which many or most of the trees lose their leaves. Tropical seasonal forests are most extensive in India and Southeast Asia, but related forests occur in all the major tropical areas.

Plate 1. Mount Kenya, Africa, the head of Teleki Valley at about 4,200 m. Tropical alpine vegetation of the paramo type (formation-type 15) gives way upward to alpine rock and snow desert (formation-type 20) on the higher slopes of the mountain. The rosette-shrub in the lower right corner is *Senecio keniodendron,* of the sunflower family. [Photo by A. Holm, reproduced by courtesy of O. Hedberg from *Acta Phytogeogr. Suecica* **49**, 1964.]

Plate 2. Detail of paramo-like alpine meadow (formation-type 15), above the tree line at 4,250 m on Mount Kenya, Africa. The rosette-shrubs in the foreground are *Lobelia telekii; Senecio keniodendron* and tussock grasses may also be seen. [Courtesy of and copyright by C. Troll, from "Zur Physiognomik der Tropengewächse," 1958.]

Plate 3. Timberline in the Uluguru Mountains, Tanzania, at the upper limit of the elfin woodland (formation-type 8), 2,600 m, looking from alpine meadow into the dense woodland. Trees are *Podocarpus*, *Myrica*, and *Pygeum* with lichens (*Usnea*) hanging from their branches; the rosette-shrubs at the edge of the woodland are *Lobelia ulurensis*. [Courtesy of and copyright by C. Troll, from "Zur Physiognomik der Tropengewächse," 1958.]

Plate 4. A timberline in the Far North, muskeg (cool-temperate bog, formation-type 21), related to bog tundra, in an area of taiga in the Tongas National Forest, Alaska. [Courtesy of U.S. Forest Service, photo by L. Forrest, from Gleason and Cronquist, 1964.]

Plate 5. Tundra (formation-type 16), a distinctive patterned ground of earth hummocks in the High Arctic. Dwarf willow (*Salix arctica*) with sedges and grasses in the foreground, hummocks with *Cassiope tetragona* and *Dryas integrifolia* in the background, on a south southwest–facing slope of mixed glacial drift and alluvium, Alex Heiberg Island, Northwest Territories, Canada. [Courtesy of and copyright by R. E. Beschel, from *U.S. Nat. Acad. Sci. Publ.* **1287**:13–20, 1963.]

Plate 6. Temperate evergreen forest (formation-type 6). Forest of Sitka spruce (*Picea sitchensis*), Cascade Head Experimental Forest, Oregon. Although this is a low-elevation forest, its appearance is much like that of taiga (formation-type 7) in the subalpine zone of mountains. [Courtesy of U.S. Forest Service, photo by R. A. Yoder.]

Plate 7. Temperate giant rainforest (formation-type 3). Coastal redwoods (*Sequoia sempervirens*) in dense stand with undergrowth of sword-fern (*Polystichum munitum*), Jedediah Smith Redwoods State Park, California. The coastal redwoods in California are the southernmost extension of the giant rainforests of the Northwest Coast of the United States, adapted to a less humid climate than that of the rainforests of the Olympic Peninsula. The redwoods are limited to a coastal belt in which fog moderates the effect of summers with little or no rainfall. [Reproduced by permission of Philip Hyde, Taylorsville, Calif.]

Plate 8. Temperate deciduous forest (formation-type 5). Southern Appalachian cove forest or mixed mesophytic forest with tulip poplar (*Liriodendron tulipifera*) dominant, Chattahoochee National Forest, Georgia. Such forests include far more tree and undergrowth species than the coastal rainforests. They are probably (along with comparable forests of eastern Asia) richest in species of temperate forests of the world and most like temperate forests of wide extent in the Northern Hemisphere in Tertiary time. [Courtesy of U.S. Forest Service, photo by Philip Archibald.]

Plate 9. Temperate woodland (formation-type 11). An extensive stand of pygmy conifer woodland dominated by juniper and piñon pine with shrub and grass undergrowth, near Flagstaff, Arizona. Climate too dry for true forest is expressed in the small size and open growth of the trees. [Courtesy of U.S. Forest Service, photo by Clime, from Gleason and Cronquist, 1964.]

Plate 10. Temperate shrubland (formation-type 12). Hard chaparral, fire-adapted communities of chamise (*Adenostoma fasciculatum*), manzanita (*Arctostaphylos* spp.), and other evergreen shrubs in the mediterranean (dry-summer) climate of southern California, Angeles National Forest. [Courtesy of U.S. Forest Service, photo by C. Miller, from Gleason and Cronquist, 1964.]

Plate 11. Temperate woodland (formation-type 11). Open woodland of evergreen oaks with a grassy undergrowth on foothills of the western slope of the Sierra Nevada, part of the extensive woodland belt surrounding the Central Valley of California. [Courtesy of U.S. Forest Service, photo by A. Gaskill.]

Plate 12. Savanna (formation-type 13) of widely scattered trees in tropical grassland. East African game plains, Olduvai, Tanzania. [Reproduced by permission of E. S. Ross, Calif. Acad. Sci., San Francisco.]

Plate 13. Temperate grassland (formation-type 14), a mixed-grass prairie in central Nebraska. [Courtesy of U.S. Forest Service, photo by B. W. Muir, from Gleason and Cronquist, 1964.]

Plate 14. Cool-temperate desert scrub (formation-type 19). Sagebrush semi-desert dominated by big sagebrush (*Artemisia tridentata*) and bluebunch wheatgrass (*Agropyron spicatum*), near Big Butte, Idaho. [Courtesy of U.S. Forest Service, photo by J. F. Pechanec, from Gleason and Cronquist, 1964.]

Plate 15. An open thorn scrub (formation-type 10) in the Mareb Valley near Teramni, Eritrea. This African vegetation is in many ways convergent with the warm-temperate desert scrub shown in Figure 2·6. The tall succulent is *Euphorbia abyssinica;* it is not a cactus but is convergent in form with the giant cactus in Figure 2·6. The flat-topped tree is *Acacia etbaica;* mesquite (*Prosopis juliflora*) is similar in form in the Arizona desert. The rosette-shrub in the foreground is *Aloe abessinica,* convergent in form with *Agave palmeri* and other species in the Arizona deserts. [Courtesy of and copyright by C. Troll, from "Zur Physiognomik der Tropengewächse," 1958.]

Plate 16. Subtropical desert (formation-type 17). Extreme desert with dunes and few plants, Namib Desert, South-West Africa. [Reproduced by permission of E. S. Ross, Calif. Acad. Sci., San Francisco.]

(3, 4) Temperate rainforests occur as giant forests (3) along the Pacific Coast of North America in a belt from the coast redwood forests of California and Oregon to the mixed coniferous rainforests of the Olympic Peninsula of Washington. The climate is cool and maritime, with abundant winter rainfall and much summer cloudiness and fog. These Pacific Coast forests are (along with Australian temperate rainforests of *Eucalyptus regnans*) the tallest forests in the world, but their low diversity of plant and animal life contrasts with the richness of tropical rainforests. Other temperate rainforests (4) of quite different structure occur as montane forests and thickets in tropical mountains, dominated by smaller broad-leaved evergreen trees, and forests of southern beech and needle-leaved trees in New Zealand and Chile (Plate 7).

(5) Temperate deciduous forests grow in moderately humid, continental, temperate zone climates, with summer rainfall and severe winters. Broad-leaved deciduous trees—oaks, beech, maples, ash, basswood, and so on—are dominant in forests that in their best development are of a size comparable to tropical rainforests, with trees to 30 and 40 m tall. Animal life of temperate deciduous forests is abundant but strongly seasonal in activity; diversity of plant and animal species is moderately low to moderately high. Mammals are primarily grounddwelling; deer are the most characteristic large herbivores in the northern Temperate Zone. Temperate deciduous forests are extensively developed in the eastern United States, in Europe, and eastern Asia, and are of more local occurrence in the Middle American highlands and Chile (Plate 8).

(6) Temperate evergreen forests occur in varied temperate zone circumstances. Sclerophyll forests of less humid, maritime (summer dry) climates are dominated by trees with tough, evergreen, relatively small, broad leaves. Extensive needle-leaved evergreen forests occur in continental climates of the western United States, and in places where soil characteristics, or fire frequency, or both favor pines over broadleaved trees in the eastern United States and western Europe. Mixed evergreen forests of both needle-leaved and sclerophyll trees occur in northern California and southern Oregon, and some other areas. Temperate evergreen forests dominated by southern pines (*Araucaria,* and so on), southern beeches (*Nothofagus* species), and in Australia by *Eucalyptus* species, occur in the Southern Hemisphere (Plate 6).

(7, 8) Subarctic-subalpine needle-leaved forests or taiga (7) are often separated from the temperate evergreen forests as a biome-type of the cold edge of the climatic range of forests. Spruces, firs, larches, or pines are dominant in most such forests; in many, dominance is shared by a spruce and a fir species. In arid mountains open pine woodlands occur in the subalpine zone; in humid areas extensive bog or muskeg may occur. The taiga extends around the world in the northern part of North America and Eurasia and extends to the south at higher elevations in mountains. Elfin woodlands (8) are subalpine communities of the tropics, of very different structure from the taiga (Plates 3, 6).

(9, 10) Thorn woodlands and thorn scrubs occupy tropical climates more arid than those of seasonal forests. Acacias and other spiny plants of the pea family are most widespread as dominants. A wide range of communities is involved, of which it is desirable to distinguish at least (9) thorn forests and woodlands, tropical communities with small or medium-sized trees in open growth with grassy undergrowth, and (10) thorn scrub dominated by large shrubs, often in dense growth, in still drier climates transitional to desert climates (Plate 15).

(11) Temperate woodlands are communities of small trees, generally of open growth in the sense that there is space between the crowns and canopy coverage is well below 100 per cent. Most woodlands have well-developed grass or shrub undergrowth. Dominant trees may be of any of the three growth-forms—needle-leaved trees, sclerophylls, and deciduous broad-leaved trees—or any combination of these. Pygmy conifer woodlands (dominated by piñon and juniper) are a widespread and distinctive community type in the western United States, oak woodlands occur in the Great Valley of California and the Cross Timbers of Texas, and evergreen oak and oak–pine wodlands are extensive in the southwestern states and Mexico. Structurally related communities occur around the Mediterranean and in the southern continents. Woodlands are most extensive in climates too dry for true forests; toward still drier climates woodlands give way to grassland, shrubland, and semidesert (Plates 9, 11).

(12) Temperate shrublands. Sclerophyll shrublands develop in climates of the Mediterranean type—moderately dry, warm temperate, maritime climates with little or no summer rain. Sclerophyll leaves (see number 6) prevail. Size and coverage of the shrubs range from arborescent (2–5 m tall) with a closed canopy, to below 1 m and quite open, in response to moisture and other factors. Mediterranean *maquis* and California chaparral are best known among such communities; equivalent biomes occur in South Africa, Chile, and West and South Australia. The dominant plants are affected by frequent fires, which burn off the aboveground stems, and then regrowth occurs from root systems that survive the fire. Other temperate zone shrublands often treated as separate formations include the chaparral-like deciduous shrublands of some inland mountain areas, the aromatic shrubland of drier mediterranean climates (garrigue, soft chaparral), heaths mostly of cooler maritime climates, and distinctive shrublands in the southern hemisphere (Plate 10).

(13) Savannas are tropical grasslands, with or without an open tree stratum. Savannas are most extensive in Africa, where they support the richest fauna of grazing animals in the world; equivalent, less extensive, and less rich communities occur in Australia, South America, and southern Asia. Some of the African and Australian savannas occur in climates too dry for forest; but soil conditions or fire, or both, rather than climate probably cause the appearance of savannas in less arid climates, particularly in South America. Both savannas and temperate grasslands are subject to fires, which affect the structure of the community and its extent into climates that might otherwise support forest (Plate 12).

(14) Temperate grasslands include the great prairies, plains, and desert grasslands of North America and the steppes of Eurasia. Temperate grasslands occur also in Africa (veldt) and South America (pampas), but grassy woodlands with eucalypts occur in most of the comparable climates of Australia. Despite reduction of vegetation structure to a single major stratum, plant species-diversity in grasslands can be high compared with most forests. Bird life is more limited than in forests because of the lack of marked stratal differentiation; mammalian faunas are characterized by the smaller burrowing and larger running herbivores. Ecological equivalents on different continents among the latter include the bison and prongbuck in North America, the wild horse and ass and saga antelope of Eurasia, the larger kangaroos of Australia, and the zebras, antelopes, and others of the rich warm-temperate grasslands of Africa (Plate 13).

(15, 16) Arctic and alpine communities. Alpine grasslands (15) include, as already indicated, the mostly sedge-dominated alpine meadows of the North Temperate Zone and the tussock grasslands and paramos of the tropics and Southern Hemisphere. Tundras (16) are the treeless arctic plains, vegetation of which may form varied and often complex patterns of dominance by dwarf-shrubs, sedges and grasses, mosses, and lichens. The tundras of North America and Eurasia are quite similar; principal herbivorous mammals include the musk ox, caribou (and reindeer of Eurasia), arctic hare, and lemming. In many tundras and some alpine communities the deeper layers of the soil are permanently frozen, and only the surface soil is thawed and becomes biologically active during the summer. In many of these communities also repeated freezing and thawing of the soil separates rocks from finer soil materials and arranges the rocks in parallel stripes, or in networks with polygonal cells; striking internal patterning of the plant communities in relation to soil differences results. In both biome-types vegetation cover decreases toward the sparse lichen communities, rock fields, and ice of high elevations and most severe climates of the Arctic and Antarctic (Plates 1–5).

(17–20) Deserts occur on all continents and include a wide range of communities. It is appropriate to distinguish: (17) tropical and subtropical deserts, influenced by very stable maritime subtropic air masses on the east sides of ocean basins, some of them with very meager plant life; (18) warm-temperate deserts, represented in North America by the widespread creosote bush communities and the floristically rich desert uplands of the Chihuahuan and Sonoran deserts; (19) cool-temperate desert scrub, including the sagebrush semidesert of the Great Basin in the United States and closely parallel communities in Asia, and (20) arctic-alpine deserts determined by the extreme cold of high latitudes and altitudes (Plates 14, 16, and 1).

(21–25) Hydric communities are adapted to very wet soils. Cool-temperate sphagnum bog (21) occurs as a local type in some areas, but can also become prevailing vegetation in such cool, humid, maritime climates as those of the blanket bogs of Scotland and Ireland. Other hydric types determined by local excess of soil moisture are not climatic types, but some are sufficiently extensive to be recognized as formations: tropical (22) and temperate (23) fresh-water swamp forests, the mangrove swamps (24) of tropical coasts and estuaries, and the saltmarshes (25) of temperate coasts (Plate 4).

Figure 3·8 arranges the formation-types into a pattern in relation to major climatic gradients. Boundaries between types cannot be located exactly because: (a) Many formations intergrade continuously. (b) Adaptations of the different growth-forms in different continents are not perfectly convergent. Some of the Australian eucalypt trees, for example, can form forests in climates that support only grassland and shrubland on other continents. (c) Climate is not solely responsible for determining what formation occurs in an area. Different soil conditions or exposure to frequent fires can determine which of two formations, both adapted to the climate of an area, can occur there. (d) A major aspect of climate affecting community structure cannot be included in Figure 3·8; this is the contrast of maritime with continental climates. The same total annual precipitation can support an evergreen forest in the maritime climate of California, a broad-leaf deciduous forest in the continental climate of Missouri. A smaller amount can support chaparral in coastal southern California, pygmy conifer woodland in the continental climate of Nevada, or dry grassland on the Great Plains.

The pattern is a considerable simplification and yet expresses some of the broad relations of natural communities, and hence of possibilities for man's use of the land, to world climates. Ecoclines 2 and 3 (Figures 3·7A and B) cross the pattern vertically from forest to desert, ecocline 2 at temperatures near 16°C and ecocline 3 near 25°C. Ecoclines 4 and 5 (Figures 3·7C and D) cross it from left to right in rain-

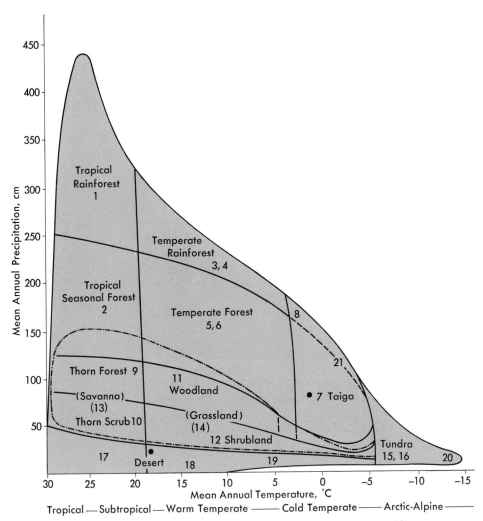

Figure 3·8. A pattern of world formation-types in relation to climatic humidity and temperature. The numbers refer to formation-types described in the text. Boundaries between types are, for a number of reasons, approximate. In climates between forest and desert, maritime versus continental climate, soil effects, and fire effects can shift the balance between woodland, shrubland, and grassland types. The dot-and-dash line encloses a wide range of environments in which either grassland, or one of the types dominated by woody plants, may form the prevailing vegetation in different areas. (Cf. Dansereau, 1957, p. 100, Lieth, *Ber. Deut. Bot. Ges.*, **69**:169, 1956, and Holdridge, *Science*, **105**:367, 1947.)

forest climates and forest climates, respectively. The vegetation pattern for the Santa Catalina Mountains (Figure 3·4) crosses obliquely between the dots indicated in taiga and in desert.

Community-wide Adaptation

Most biomes on land are dominated by a number of plant species of the same growth-form. In many cases these plants are members of different genera and families, which have independently evolved from other plants of different growth-forms—they are products of evolutionary convergence. Convergence is most conspicuous in the tropical rainforest, in which a hundred tree species of closely similar form and foliage may occur in a forest tract. Competition for a place in the canopy in this most consistently favorable environment exerts a constraint on form in these plants. Trees that succeed are of only a narrow range of forms and leaf types, however much they may differ in height and presumably in soil requirements and relations to other species. Phenomena of evolutionary convergence are impressive also in communities subject to severe environmental problems. Two communities that are alike in the importance of community-wide adaptative problems and unlike in most other respects—the desert and the plankton—may illustrate such phenomena.

Few deserts are really barren of life, and some have rich plant and animal life. All the organisms must in some way come to terms with the environmental limitation that is responsible for the occurrence of desert (excluding cold deserts)—shortage of water. In deserts the shortage of water available to organisms is usually combined with high daytime temperatures and low air humidities, which tend to cause rapid loss of water by evaporation. Desert organisms must maintain a balanced water budget: intake must equal loss if the amount of water in the organisms is to remain sufficient to support life. The balance must be maintained in an environment that makes the balance difficult on both sides—chronic limitation of income combined with continued tendency to overexpenditure by evaporation and other loss.

Adaptations among desert animals include

1. Increasing water intake by eating plant tissues with high water content, such as cacti, drinking of dew, traveling to waterholes.
2. In some arthropods, direct uptake of water from the air, when relative humidity is over 80 per cent.
3. Efficient use of the metabolic water from respiration of food.
4. Reduction of water loss by excretion and egestion of concentrated urine and nearly dry feces.
5. Impermeable body coverings.
6. Behavior that reduces water loss, such as inactivity and use of shade, and often sheltering underground, during the times of highest temperatures.

Desert arthropods reduce loss by impermeable coverings and accept rise of body temperatures to levels that would be lethal to vertebrates; small mammals must be nocturnal to avoid combined heat stress and water loss, which for them is intolerable above ground in the daytime; large mammals that cannot hide below ground must control body temperature by surface evaporation of water and must replace this water.

Adaptations that appear in different desert plants include

1. Deep or wide-ranging roots for effective water uptake.
2. Water storage tissues in cacti and other succulent plants.
3. Reduction of water loss from leaves by waxy protective coatings and surface hairs, by gray leaf color in some (reducing the effect of sunlight in heating the leaf), and by effective stomatal function.
4. Reduction of water loss by reducing amount of leaf surface, or by shedding leaves (or branches) in the dry season.
5. Use of the stem surface for auxiliary photosynthesis or all photosynthesis.
6. "Reversed" diurnal function of stomata and metabolism in succulents, so that the stomata are open and CO_2 is taken in and fixed (as malate) by night, the CO_2 being available for photosynthesis during the daytime when stomatal openings and CO_2 intake are less.
7. Tolerance of the tissues to reduced water content even, in some club mosses and ferns, to a nearly air-dry condition of foliage.
8. Ability, because of the tolerance of water loss and consequent higher osmotic concentration in tissues, to take up water from relatively dry soils.
9. Timing of growth to use water when available, with avoidance of exposure to loss during the dry season.

The last adaptation appears, for example, in annual herbs, which grow rapidly to flower and fruit during the rainy season and spend the dry season as seeds, and in perennial herbs, which survive the dry season as roots that grow aboveground foliage during the rainy season. Survival for the hundreds of species of annual plants of deserts requires systems of inherited metabolic triggers for germination and flowering, neatly adjusted to control timing of these in relation to amount and duration of rainfall and seasonal temperatures and day lengths.

Protoplasm is a little heavier than water, per unit volume. Organisms of the plankton, which live suspended in the water of lakes and the seas, consequently tend to sink until they fall below the lighted zone that supports most active plankton life. There is, in fact, a steady loss of organisms from the upper plankton by sinking, and the living and dead plankton organisms that sink to the depths of lakes and the oceans are the nutrient rain that supports much of the life of the depths. Plankton organisms can variously solve or mitigate the sinking problem.

1. Small size, which reduces sinking rates in bacteria and unicellular algae—the dust-particle approach.
2. In larger forms, development of bristles and projections that reduce sinking rates—the feather approach.
3. Flattened or umbrella-shaped form that reduces sinking rates as in jellyfish—the parachute approach.
4. Reduction of the specific gravity of the organism by various devices —oil droplets in copepods and diatoms, gas bubbles in blue-green algae and protozoans, large amounts of water in gelatinous sheaths and the tissues of jellyfish.
5. Active swimming upward, which is necessary, despite other adaptations, in most plankton animals.

Two principles may be observed in these community-wide adaptations. First, the problem is normally met by no single device but by a combination of the approaches mentioned. Thus a plankton jellyfish combines parachute form with low specific gravity and upward swimming. A cactus combines stem photosynthesis and low surface area with stomatal and metabolic adaptation to use the CO_2 taken in at night, and with rapid water uptake during rain and storage in succulent tissue, although the latter adaptation has required in addition the evolution of spines to provide some protection against animals that eat succulent tissue in adaptation to their own problems of water balance. Adaptation is usually based not on a single device but on a pattern or design of interrelated adaptive devices. Second, the species in a community show some convergences but also the most varied patterns of adaptation, using different combinations of devices to solve the same environmental problem. Such diversity of adaptive pattern is related to the diversity of the niches occupied by the species. Freshwater rapids, sandy beaches, rocky marine shores, and the tundra are other ecosystems with diverse adaptive patterns in response to severe environmental problems.

Succession

As a lake fills with silt it changes gradually from a deep to a shallow lake or pond, then to a marsh, and beyond this, in some cases, to a dry-land forest. When in an area of forests a farm field is abandoned, a series of plant communities grow up and replace one another—first annual weeds, then perennial weeds and grasses, then shrubs, and trees —until a forest ends the development. If a landslide exposes a surface of rock in the mountains, the surface may be successively occupied by a sparse cover of lichens; a spreading moss mat; grasses, which enter and become a meadow; a shrub thicket, which overtops and suppresses the grasses; a first forest stage of smaller trees, which seed into the shrub thicket, grow through it, and replace it; and a final stage of larger trees, which take dominance from the first trees and may form a larger and potentially permanent forest community.

Such processes of community development are called *successions*. In the first example the principal cause of the change in the community was a physical process—the filling in of the lake with silt. In the second example, a principal cause was the growth of plants on an existing soil. In the third the succession proceeded by a back-and-forth interplay between organisms and environment: as one dominant species modified the soil and microclimate in ways that made possible the entry of a second species, which became dominant and modified environment in ways that suppressed the first and made possible the entry of a third dominant, which in turn altered its environment. Causes of successional changes are, to varying degrees, external to the community or internal to the community; many successions involve both kinds of causes and reciprocal influences. In any case a gradient of changing environment and a gradient of changing species populations and community characteristics parallel one another. A succession is an ecocline in time.

A number of trends or progressive developments underlie most successional processes.

1. There is usually progressive development of the soil, with increasing depth, increasing organic content, and increasing differentiation of layers or horizons toward the mature soil of the final community.
2. The height, massiveness, and differentiation into strata of the plant community increase.
3. Productivity, the rate of formation of organic matter per unit area in the community, increases with increasing development of the soil and of community structure and increasing utilization by the community of environmental resources.
   microclimate within the community is increasingly determined by characteristics of the community itself.
4. As height and density of aboveground plant cover increase, the
5. Species-diversity increases from the simple communities of early succession to the richer communities of late succession.
6. Populations rise and fall and replace one another along the time gradient in a manner much like that in stable communities along

environmental gradients (Figure 3·2). The rate of this replacement in many cases slows through the course of succession as smaller and shorter-lived species are replaced by larger and longer-lived ones.

7. Relative stability of the communities consequently increases. Early stages are in some cases of evident instability, with populations rapidly replacing one another; the final community is usually stable, dominated by longer-lived plants, which maintain their populations with community composition no longer changing directionally.

It is in some cases possible to drive the successional process backwards by disturbing a community. A grassland under heavy grazing may show first a reduction in coverage of the plants most palatable to the cattle. With continued grazing the total grass coverage is reduced, the more palatable plant species disappear, and weeds that may be almost absent from the undisturbed grassland appear and spread. With continued grazing and trampling, most of the grass may be destroyed and, despite the unpalatable weeds that survive, the soil is exposed to erosion. The end result of the process may be, depending on topographic position and soil, a mud field with erosion channels or a rocky mountain slope stripped of much of its soil. Thus by severe and continued disturbance all the trends of succession—soil development, community stature, productivity, diversity, stability, and extent of modification of environment by community—have been reversed toward zero.

Probably some partial reversals of these trends occur during normal, progressive successions. Productivity and species-diversity, in particular, are thought to decrease from late successional stages into the climax community in many cases. Despite these reversals, and despite a wide range of variations in communities and successions, there are broad parallels in the character of ecoclines of three sorts. The trends described apply in many respects to (a) present environmental gradients from extreme environments (as of the desert and arctic) to favorable ones, (b) successions, and (c) community retrogression under persistent adverse environmental pressure—continued excessive harvest as in overgrazing, exposure to toxic chemicals as in some cases of industrial pollution, and exposure to chronic ionizing radiation as in experiments with irradiation of forests.

Climax

The community that ends a succession is termed a *climax*. Central to the concept of climax is the community's relative stability. The populations of a climax community show some irregular fluctuation in time because of environmental change and the character of population processes, and some climaxes show more regular or cyclic fluctuation. In the climax, however, these are fluctuations around a stable, relatively constant, mean condition. Stability of the climax (like that of a desert animal's body water) entails balances maintained in the function of a dynamic, living system.

For a species population in a climax community to be stable, there must be a balance between natality and mortality, between income of new individuals by reproduction and outgo of individuals by death. Ideally, such balances of natality and mortality would, over longer periods at least, characterize all the species populations of the climax community. The balance should also apply to the intake and release of matter and energy by the community as a whole. This kind of constancy in the system, based on a balancing of income and outgo and superimposed on an underlying flow through the system, is known as a *dynamic equilibrium* or *steady state*. A pool along a stream provides a simple illustration of the concept, which is of fundamental significance in all levels of biological systems from protoplasmic function to the community and ecosystem. Water flows through the pool but, with equal rates of inflow and outflow, the pool itself as an object or system stays the same—in steady state. *Climax* implies a steady-state condition in a natural community.

Application of the concept to natural communities in the field is not, however, all that simple. Ecologists can use evidences on self-maintenance of communities (absence of indications of disturbance or of replacement of populations, consistency of communities in similar habitats) to judge whether communities may be climax. Broader interpretations of climax entail two other general observations. The first of these is a degree of convergence among the successions of a given area. The pond, old field, and rock surface successions may all end in forests. Many successions in a given area converge from disparate beginnings toward similar, though not necessarily identical, end stages. From this observation one might infer that all successions in an area will ultimately converge toward a single climax community, which is determined by the climate of the area and may be termed *climatic climax*. This interpretation (the monoclimax theory) was of great importance in the development of ecology and is still, with modifications appropriate to the second observation, applied by some ecologists.

The second observation is that vegetation of most areas is complex, including, even when undisturbed by man, a number of types of stable communities. Different stable communities normally occur on south-facing and north-facing slopes, and on rocks differing in chemical composition and forming soils with different characteristics (for example limestone versus granite, or serpentine versus other rocks). The convergence of successions is partial; substantial differences remain among the climaxes which develop in different habitats. An area will contain a number of kinds of climax communities forming a mosaic corresponding to the mosaic of habitats, as well as various successional communities. In this interpretation (polyclimax theory) the stable and undisturbed community type that is most extensive in different habitats, including those of intermediate environmental conditions for the area, may be termed climatic climax. Community stability and regional prevalence are thus recognized separately, but the climatic climax combines these. Other local climaxes occur in habitats of more extreme topographic situations and distinctive soil effects.

It is but a step from the polyclimax to the climax pattern interpretation. A climax is a steady-state community the characteristics of which are determined by the characteristics of its own habitat. Habitats and the communities that develop in them intergrade as ecoclines. Despite the occurrence of disturbances and discontinuities, climax communities may be interpreted as not so much a mosaic, as a pattern of intergrading communities corresponding to a pattern of environmental gradients. The central or most extensive (steady-state, undisturbed) community type in the pattern is its prevailing or climatic climax and expresses the climate of the area. It is by using prevailing climaxes as means of abstraction from the full complexity of actual community patterns that we can relate communities to climate in major ecoclines and geographic patterns.

Summary

In almost any area of the earth's surface not too much modified by man a complex pattern of natural communities and environments, or habitats of these communities, may be observed. Habitats and communities intergrade along environmental gradients; a gradient of environments together with the corresponding community gradient is an ecosystem gradient, or ecocline. The research technique called *gradient analysis* deals with relations of gradients of environment, species populations, and community characteristics to one another in ecoclines and in community patterns. When species are studied along ecoclines, their populations are found to have scattered positions along the gradient and broadly overlapping, bell-shaped distributions. Species appear to evolve toward difference of habitat, as well as of niche, and consequently toward scattering of their population centers in relation to environmental gradients. The great richness in species of the living world is a product of evolution toward both niche differentiation and habitat differentiation, in the wide range of environments and geographic areas of the world.

The variation in communities of a given area is generally affected by two or more environmental gradients and ecoclines, for example, elevation and topographic moisture gradient in mountains. The ecoclines can be used as axes in relation to which the communities of the area form a pattern, and in this pattern of communities and ecosystems we can relate to one another the patterns of (a) environmental gradients and habitats, (b) species distributions, which form together a complex population continuum, (c) characteristics of communities, and (d) the types of communities we choose to recognize. Community patterns of this sort are often used to analyze stable, mature, or climax communities only. In any particular habitat in the landscape, however, the climax community may have been destroyed or may not yet have developed. In this habitat the communities go through a progressive development of parallel and interacting changes in environments and communities, a succession. Through the course of succession community production, height, and mass, species-diversity, relative stability, and soil depth and differentiation all tend to increase (though there are exceptions). The end point of succession is a climax community of relatively stable species composition and steady-state function, adapted to its habitat and essentially permanent in its habitat if undisturbed.

The complexity of communities in a landscape thus involves a pattern of intergrading climax communities, the continuities of which may be interrupted by local discontinuities of topography and soil, as well as by disturbance and successional communities. It is generally possible to recognize, however, a climax community that is central to the range of variation and is most widespread among the stable communities of the area; this principal community type for the area is the prevailing or climatic climax. The prevailing climax is adapted to the climate of the area, and by means of prevailing climaxes we can relate communities to environments on another level, in terms of broad geographic and altitudinal ecoclines in relation to climates. The gradient from forests to oak woodlands, to grasslands, and finally to deserts along the rainfall gradient westward in temperate climates of the United States is such a major ecocline. Each of the four major community types along this ecocline, when these are defined by vegetation structure and not by species composition, is a biome. Convergent adaptations to environment appear among the organisms of a given community, and also in the kinds of communities, or biomes, that appear in similar environments in different parts of the world. A grouping of communities of different continents that are of similar structure in adaptation to similar environments is a biome-type. Climatic adaptation of natural communities throughout the world can be interpreted in terms of a pattern of biome-types (and of the major ecoclines that connect these) corresponding to a pattern of climatic gradients.

References

Billings, D. W. (1964) *Plants and the Ecosystem*. Belmont, Calif.: Wadsworth. v + 154 pp.

Curtis, John T. (1959) *The Vegetation of Wisconsin: An Ordination of Plant Communities*. Madison: University of Wisconsin. xi + 657 pp.

Dansereau, Pierre. (1957) *Biogeography: An Ecological Perspective*. New York: Ronald. xiii + 394 pp.

Eyre, S. R. (1963) *Vegetation and Soils, A World Picture*. Chicago: Aldine. xvi + 324 pp.

Gleason, Henry A., and Arthur Cronquist. (1964) *The Natural Geography of Plants*. New York and London: Columbia University. viii + 420 pp.

Hesse, Richard, W. C. Allee, and K. P. Schmidt. (1951) *Ecological Animal Geography*, 2nd Eng. ed. New York: Wiley; London: Chapman & Hall. xiii + 715 pp.

Kendeigh, S. Charles. (1961) *Animal Ecology*. Englewood Cliffs, N.J.: Prentice-Hall. x + 468 pp.

Kormondy, Edward J., editor. (1965) *Readings in Ecology*. Englewood Cliffs, N. J.: Prentice-Hall. xiv + 219 pp.

Küchler, A. W. (1964) *Potential Natural Vegetation of the Conterminous United States*. New York: Amer. Geographical Soc., Special Publ. no. **36**, v + 156 pp., map.

Odum, Eugene P., and H. T. Odum. (1959) *Fundamentals of Ecology*, 2nd ed. Philadelphia and London: Saunders. xvii + 546 pp.

Oosting, Henry J. (1956) *The Study of Plant Communities*, 2nd ed. San Francisco: Freeman. viii + 440 pp.

Ricketts, Edward F., Jack Calvin, and Joel W. Hedgpeth. (1962) *Between Pacific Tides*, 3rd ed. Stanford: University Press. xiii + 516 pp.

Rumney, George R. (1968) *Climatology and the World's Climates*. New York and London: Macmillan. x + 656 pp.

Tansley, A. G. (1939) *The British Islands and Their Vegetation*. Cambridge: University Press. 1965 repr., 2 vols., xxxviii + 930 pp.

Beard, J. S. (1944) "Climax vegetation in tropical America." *Ecology*, **25**:127–158.

Beard, J. S. (1955) "The classification of tropical American vegetation-types." *Ecology*, **36**:89–100.

Dyksterhuis, E. J. (1948) "Condition and management of range land based on quantitative ecology." *Journal of Range Management*, **2**:104–115.

Edney, E. B. (1967) "Water balance in desert arthropods." *Science*, **156**:1059–1066.

Fager, E. W., and J. A. McGowan. (1963) "Zooplankton species groups in the North Pacific." *Science,* **140**:453–460.

Gleason, Henry A. (1939) "The individualistic concept of the plant association." *American Midland Naturalist,* **21**:92–110.

Margalef, R. (1963) "On certain unifying principles in ecology." *American Naturalist,* **97**:357–374.

McIntosh, R. P. (1958) "Plant communities." *Science,* **128**:115–120.

Merriam, C. H. (1898) "Life zones and crop zones of the United States." *U.S. Biological Survey Bulletin,* **10**:1–79.

Stephenson, T. A., and A. Stephenson. (1949) "The universal features of zonation between tide-marks on rocky coasts." *Journal of Ecology.* **37**:289–305.

Troll, C. (1961) "Klima und Pflanzenkleid der Erde in dreidimensionaler Sicht." *Naturwissenschaften,* **48**:332–348.

Whittaker, R. H. (1953) "A consideration of climax theory: the climax as a population and pattern." *Ecological Monographs,* **23**:41–78.

Whittaker, R. H. (1967) "Gradient analysis of vegetation." *Biological Reviews,* **42**:207–264.

Whittaker, R. H., and W. A. Niering. (1965) "Vegetation of the Santa Catalina Mountains, Arizona: a gradient analysis of the south slope." *Ecology,* **46**:429–452.

Whittaker, R. H., and W. A. Niering. (1968) "Vegetation of the Santa Catalina Mountains, Arizona. IV. Limestone and acid soils." *Journal of Ecology,* **56**:523–544.

Whittaker, R. H., R. B. Walker, and A. R. Kruckeberg. (1954) "The ecology of serpentine soils." *Ecology,* **35**:258–288.

Woodwell, G. M. (1967) "Radiation and the patterns of nature." *Science,* **156**:461–470.

4

Production

Production Measurement

THE EARTH IS ILLUMINATED by sunlight, the energy of which averages 700 calories per square centimeter of the earth's surface per day for all wave lengths on the outside of the atmosphere, about 55 kCal/cm²/yr in the visible range within the atmosphere at the earth's surface. Man is harvesting organic material as a combine moves across a field of wheat, a trawler lifts its net from the sea, and a logging company works through a forest. Sunlight and harvest are connected by the function of ecosystems in binding energy into organic material—their *productivity,* on which man, like all animals, is wholly dependent for his life.

Primary productivity is the rate at which energy is bound or organic material created by photosynthesis, per unit of the earth's surface per unit time; it is most often expressed as energy in cal/cm²/yr, or dry organic matter in g/m²/yr (g/m² × 8.92 = lbs/acre). Productivity, which is a rate, is to be clearly distinguished from the amount of organic matter present at a given time, per unit of the earth's surface. The latter is standing crop or *biomass,* and is usually expressed as dry g/m² or kg/m², or as t/ha (metric tons, 10⁶ g, per hectare, 10⁴m²). Primary productivity is the consequence of photosynthesis by green plants (including algae in which the green of chlorophyll is masked by other colors). Bacterial photosynthesis and chemosynthesis may also contribute to primary productivity but are generally of small significance. The green plants are using for their own respiration part of the organic matter they create. The total energy bound, or organic matter created, by green plants per unit surface and time is their *gross* primary productivity. The amount of energy bound or organic matter created, per unit surface and time, that is left after the respiration of these plants is their *net* primary productivity. Only the net primary productivity is available for harvest by man or other animals. Productivities of heterotrophic organisms—animals and saprobes—in communities are termed *secondary productivities*.

A description of some means of measurement may clarify these concepts. The net primary production of a farm field planted in a cereal crop may, for example, be sought. At the end of the growing season the plants, with roots, are removed from a number of sample areas in the field. (Actually, samples are taken through the growing season to determine loss of old leaves, insect consumption, weed production, and so on.) The plants are dried and weighed by fractions, and the net primary productivity of the field may look like this:
Net primary production in grams = stems (148) + leaves (72) + flowers and fruits (87) + roots (46) + loss to insects (2) − seed sown (5) = 350 dry g/m^2/yr = 1,500 kCal/m^2/yr. (Energy equivalents to dry weight net production are based on bomb calorimetric measurements for different tissues. Land plant tissues average around 4.25 kCal/dry g, animal tissues around 5.0 kCal/dry g. For gross productivity there are complications affecting the relations of photosynthetic energy to CO_2 assimilation and ATP bonds, respiration in light and dark, and dry-weight production equivalents that will not be treated here.)

This approach, the harvest method, is simple and reliable when annual plants are in question and these can be fully harvested. The harvest method can also be applied to natural grasslands but with additional difficulties, particularly as regards plant parts (roots, rhizomes, and so on) that live more than one year. Forest plantations, in which the trees have been planted by man and are all of the same age, can be dealt with by the harvest method. A forest fifty years old may be cut and sample roots dug up, and the dry weight of the trees with roots per unit area determined. This value (a biomass value) divided by fifty is an incomplete expression of mean net production per year. It must be corrected for annual production and loss of leaves, flowers, and fruits, for animal harvest, for death and loss of branches and roots, and for death of whole trees, if any. Study of a series of plantations—five, ten, twenty, thirty-five, and fifty years of age, say—may make these corrections possible.

Study of net production of natural forests and shrub communities, which have plants of many different ages, requires a different approach. In the technique of forest dimension analysis,

1. The trees in sample quadrats are measured; diameter and wood growth rate at breast height and tree height are determined for each tree.

2. A set of sample trees are cut and subjected to a detailed analysis,

from which are determined the dry weights of fractions—stem wood, stem bark, branch wood and bark, twigs and leaves, root crown and roots, flowers and fruits. By various calculations, the net annual production is obtained for each fraction. Stem volumes, leaf and bark surface areas, chlorophyll content, and other dimensions of interest are determined at the same time.

3. Logarithmic regressions are computed for the sets of trees relating the biomass and the production of each fraction to the diameter at breast height, or to other dimensions of the trees.

4. The regressions are used to compute, on the basis of its diameter, the probable biomass and production of each tree in the sample quadrat measurements of 1. These values summed give biomass and production of trees per unit area in the forest.

5. Biomass and production of shrubs and herbs of the forest undergrowth are separately determined. Larger shrubs may be measured with the same procedures as trees. Measurements for small shrubs and herbs may be based on clippings of their current growth in small sample areas and ratios of current growth weight to plant biomass and production. From these steps result the forest biomass and net production values of Table 4·1.

The net production value of 1,200 dry $g/m^2/yr$ for trees and undergrowth together is a fairly typical one for forests. Mature forests have larger fractions of their production in stems, and smaller fractions in branches, twigs and leaves, and roots, as indicated in estimates of these for a cove forest in Table 4·1. A value for gross productivity is also desired, and this may be determined by gaseous exchange measurements. Twigs with leaves are enclosed in transparent plastic chambers, and the CO_2 content of the air entering and leaving the chambers is measured. CO_2 uptake must be corrected for estimated CO_2 release by respiration at the same time. By these means, converted from the twigs in chambers to the full mass of foliage on all levels in the forest, and integrated through the year, a total photosynthetic activity or gross primary productivity may be determined. The gross productivity of the oak–pine forest is calculated as

Gross productivity = net primary productivity + plant respiration
2,650   1,200   1,450 $(g/m^2/yr)$

The forest plants thus consume in respiration 55 per cent of their gross productivity; the remaining 45 per cent is available for harvest by animals or decomposition by bacteria and fungi. For the cove forest net production of 1,390 $g/m^2/yr$ and an estimated plant respiration of 60 per cent give gross productivity of 3,500 $g/m^2/yr$.

TABLE 4·1

Net Production and Biomass in Temperate-Zone Forests—a Young Oak–Pine Forest at Brookhaven, Long Island, New York, and a Climax Deciduous Cove Forest, Great Smoky Mountains National Park, Tennessee. (Brookhaven data from an intensive study by the author and G. M. Woodwell (1968, 1969), cove forest values estimated in a study by the author, 1966)

	OAK–PINE FOREST		COVE FOREST	
	Net pro-duction	Biomass	Net pro-duction	Biomass
Totals, net production ($g/m^2/yr$) and bio-mass (kg/m^2), dry matter, for trees	1,060	9.7	1,300	58.5
Totals for undergrowth	134	0.46	90	0.135
Percentages of totals for trees in				
Stem wood	14.0	36.1	33.3	69.3
Stem bark	2.5	8.4	3.7	6.3
Branch wood and bark	23.3	16.9	13.1	10.3
Leaves	33.1	4.2	29.1	.6
Fruits and flowers	2.1	.2	1.8	.03
Roots	25.0	34.2	19.0	13.5
Biomass accumulation ratio	8.5		43.5	
Leaf area ratio, m^2/m^2	3.8		6.2	
Bark area ratio, m^2/m^2	1.5		2.1	
Chlorophyll, g/m^2	1.9		2.2	
Total respiration/gross productivity	0.80		1.0	
Age of canopy trees, years	40–45		150–400	
Mean tree height, m.	7.6		34.0	

In some circumstances diurnal curves of change in the CO_2 level in the environment provide an alternative approach. In the oak–pine forest, for example, the air is on some nights trapped beneath an inversion (of temperature increase with height above the ground). CO_2 released by respiration accumulates beneath the inversion, and this accumulation can be measured and its rate related to temperature. By integration of the rates in relation to temperature for different seasons around the year, an approximation of respiration for the whole community is obtained. The value for the oak–pine forest is 2,110 $g/m^2/yr$. Estimation of respiration by plants from the gaseous exchange chambers in the forest is 1450 $g/m^2/yr$; the remaining respiration, by animals and saprobes, is consequently 660 $g/m^2/yr$.

Eleven per cent of the weight of leaves in this forest is eaten by insects. This figure is not a secondary productivity, which must be measured by detailed studies of animal populations that we shall not describe. There is some additional harvest of shrubs by browsing deer, of roots by burrowing animals, of wood by boring insects, and of leaf litter on the ground by soil animals. It is likely that less than 10 per cent of net production is directly utilized by animals, however; whereas the remainder is utilized by saprobes (bacteria and fungi) or remains as accumulated biomass. We combine these measurements and estimates into a production balance for the forest:

Gross Productivity		Plant Respiration	Saprobe Respiration		Animal Respiration		Biomass Accumulation
2,650	=	1,450 +	580	+	80	+	540
							$(g/m^2/yr)$

Gaseous exchange and diurnal curve methods are useful also for plankton communities. The light and dark bottle technique for plankton measurement represents the former. Two bottles, one transparent and one opaque, are filled with water at a given depth of a lake or the sea, closed, maintained at that depth for a time, and brought to the surface for determination of oxygen content of the water. The decrease of oxygen in the dark bottle over the amount in the same volume of free water at the beginning of the experiment represents the respiration by plankton organisms in the bottle. The increase of oxygen in the light bottle represents release of oxygen in photosynthesis (reduced in measured amount, however, by the fact that the plankton organisms are at the same time using a smaller amount of oxygen for respiration). The sum, oxygen increase in the light bottle plus the amount of decrease in the dark bottle, expresses gross productivity. (The oxygen sum must be multiplied by 0.375 to give an equivalent carbon assimilation, and values must be integrated for different depths, around the daily cycle, and around the year. Growth of and oxygen use by bacteria on the surfaces in the bottles imply increasing error with increasing length of time the bottles are closed.)

Plankton production can be approached also by measurements using CO_2 labeled with radiocarbon, ^{14}C. Plankton samples in water of known CO_2 content are provided with $^{14}CO_2$ and kept at appropriate depths or under controlled light intensities. By separating the plankton from the water and measuring the ^{14}C content of the plankton, carbon uptake during a given period may be determined. The results are complicated by the movement of some of the radiocarbon back into the water as $^{14}CO_2$ from respiration and as organic compounds. The ^{14}C technique consequently gives a measurement between gross and net productivity, closer to gross productivity for short periods (one to three hours), approaching net productivity for longer periods (one to two days). The technique has become the standard means of measuring productivity of marine plankton, for it is more sensitive than the light-and-dark bottle technique. The diurnal curve approach can also be applied to some aquatic communities. Estimates of production based on chlorophyll content of communities combined with carbon assimilation rates per unit chlorophyll at different light intensities are possible, but are affected by differences in such assimilation rates.

Production on Land

Water, light, carbon dioxide, and soil nutrients are necessary for production on land, and temperature and successional processes affect rates of productivity. CO_2 is normally available in amounts around 0.03 per cent of the gases in the atmosphere; small variations in CO_2 content of the air are not known to have significant effects on terrestrial production. Sunlight varies in intensity, quality, and duration with latitude, altitude, and climate, but apart from length of growing season, differences in sunlight are thought less significant than other factors affecting production. Of concern are primarily effects of moisture and temperature, and secondarily those of nutrients and succession.

Plants on land need large amounts of water for transpiration because the stomata must be open if CO_2 is to be taken in, and water will be lost if the stomata are open. Water is needed also for protoplasmic content and for metabolic reactions including photosynthesis, though much the largest part of the water taken up by the plant is lost by transpiration. Availability of water is a major determinant of productivity on land. In arid climates there is a nearly linear increase in net primary production with increase in annual precipitation (Figure 4·1). In more humid forest climates the linear relation no longer applies, for there is a plateau beyond which production shows little increase, if any, with increased precipitation. The production supported by a given amount of precipitation may be affected by seasonal distribution of the precipitation and by mean temperature and annual temperature cycle. These and other factors produce the scattering of the points in Figure 4·1. Because the rate of loss of water from the soil by evaporation and transpiration is less in a cool climate, a given amount of rainfall can support vegetation of less arid character in a cool climate than in a warm one.

Normal ranges of net production for some terrestrial biome-types are indicated in Table 4·2. Extensive areas of desert and tundra produce less than 200 g/m²/yr. Temperate-zone cereal crops have productions generally in the same range as many natural grasslands and shrublands

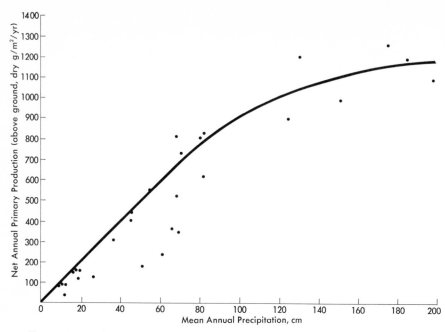

Figure 4·1. Relation of net annual primary production to rainfall. Data from various sources; peak productions of unstable communities are excluded.

—200 to 800 g/m²/yr. Hybrid corn and other crops under intensive cultivation can (like some prairies of favorable environments) exceed 1,000 g/m²/yr, and some marshlands and tropical crops exceed 3,000 g/m²/yr. Woodlands apparently mostly produce 400 to 1,000 g/m²/yr. There is broad overlap in the productivities of the intermediate biome-types—woodlands, shrublands, and grasslands—for factors other than precipitation quantity (notably seasonal distribution of precipitation, fire frequency, and soil characteristics) determine which one of these types occurs in an area. Many mature, stable temperate-zone forests of favorable environments have net productions of 1,200 to 1,500 g/m²/yr. Some forests of cold or dry environments produce less, some young forests, and probably some swamp and floodplain forests, more.

There is a general tendency for biomass, as well as production, to decrease along moisture gradients. Biomasses of mature forests are mostly in the range of 20 to 60 kg/m², woodlands 4 to 20, shrublands 2 to 10, grasslands 0.5 to 3, and deserts and tundras 0 to 2, though some values outside these ranges are reported as indicated in Table 4·2. The low biomasses of grasslands in this sequence result from the short lives of the aboveground parts of the fire-adapted plants of grasslands. Apart from grasslands, the age of dominant plants in general

Net Primary Production and Plant Biomass for Major Ecosystems and for the Earth's Surface. Prepared by the author and G. E. Likens from various sources (cf. Bowen 1966, Rodin & Bazilevich 1968, Ryther 1963, Strickland 1965) and estimates.

	AREA * 10^6 km²	NET PRIMARY PRODUCTIVITY, PER UNIT AREA † dry g/m²/yr normal range	mean	WORLD NET PRIMARY PRODUCTION ** 10^9 dry tons/yr	BIOMASS PER UNIT AREA ‡ dry kg/m² normal range	mean	WORLD BIOMASS ** 10^9 dry tons
Lake and stream	2	100–1,500	500	1.0	0–0.1	0.02	0.04
Swamp and marsh	2	800–4,000	2,000	4.0	3–50	12	24
Tropical forest	20	1,000–5,000	2,000	40.0	6–80	45	900
Temperate forest	18	600–2,500	1,300	23.4	6–200	30	540
Boreal forest	12	400–2,000	800	9.6	6–40	20	240
Woodland and shrubland	7	200–1,200	600	4.2	2–20	6	42
Savanna	15	200–2,000	700	10.5	0.2–15	4	60
Temperate grassland	9	150–1,500	500	4.5	0.2–5	1.5	14
Tundra and alpine	8	10–400	140	1.1	0.1–3	0.6	5
Desert scrub	18	10–250	70	1.3	0.1–4	0.7	13
Extreme desert, rock and ice	24	0–10	3	0.07	0–0.2	0.02	0.5
Agricultural land	14	100–4,000	650	9.1	0.4–12	1	14
Total land	149		730	109.		12.5	1,852.
Open ocean	332	2–400	125	41.5	0–0.005	0.003	1.0
Continental shelf	27	200–600	350	9.5	0.001–0.04	0.01	0.3
Attached algae and estuaries	2	500–4,000	2,000	4.0	0.04–4	1	2.0
Total ocean	361		155	55.		0.009	3.3
Total for earth	510		320	164.		3.6	1,855.

* Square kilometers × 0.3861 = square miles.
† Grams per square meter × 0.01 = t/ha, × 0.1 = dz/ha or m centn/ha (metric centers, 100 kg. per hectare, 10^4 square meters), × 10 = kg/ha, × 8.92 = lbs/acre.
** Metric tons (10^6 g) × 1.1023 = English short tons.
‡ Kilograms per square meter × 100 = dz/ha, × 10 = t/ha, × 8922 = lbs/acre, × 4.461 = English short tons per acre.

increases from deserts to climax forests (though some woodland, shrubland, and desert plants are quite old). The relation of biomass to productivity may be conveniently expressed as the biomass accumulation
ratio—the ratio of dry-weight biomass to annual net primary productivity. Such ratios (for aboveground parts of plants) increase through
the sequence of terrestrial biome-types: normal ranges are from 2 to 10
in desert, 1.5 to 3 in grasslands, 3 to 12 in shrublands, 10 to 30 in
woodlands, 20 to 50 in mature forests. It will be evident that relations
of productivity and biomass accumulation to the moisture and temperature gradients underlie some of the physiognomic trends described in
chapter 3.

Productivities decrease along the temperature gradient from the
tropics to the arctic. The relation is not, however, simply linear and is
not simply interpretable by van't Hoff or Arrhenius relations of metabolic reactions to temperature. In each temperature zone the organisms
have evolved adaptations of metabolic rates and life-cycle timings to
the temperatures and seasonal cycles they encounter. The increase in
the combined metabolism of plants of the community—primary productivity—with a 10°C increase in mean annual temperature is consequently much less than the two- to threefold increase stated by the
van't Hoff relation.

Figure 4·2 illustrates relations of forest net production to altitude

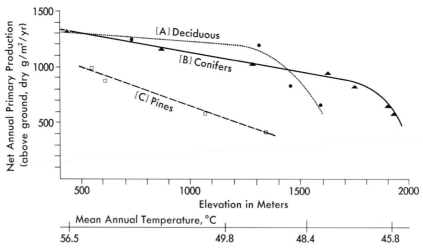

**Figure 4·2. Relation of forest net production to the elevation gradient in the
Great Smoky Mountains, Tennessee,** for **(A)** broad-leaf deciduous forests of moist
environments, **(B)** evergreen coniferous forests (hemlock, spruce, and fir) of moist environments, and **(C)** pine forests of dry environments. [Production data from Whittaker,
1966; temperatures from Shanks, Ecology, **35**:354, 1954.]

and temperature in one area, the Great Smoky Mountains. From these data it appears that

1. Net productivities of stable forests of relatively favorable moisture conditions, curves A and B, are convergent over a wide range of warm-temperate to cool-temperate climates.
2. There is a point beyond the latter at which productivity decreases more rapidly toward the low values of alpine and arctic climates.
3. Although net production of climax deciduous and evergreen forests is similar in warm-temperate climates, in the transition to the arctic and alpine climates evergreen forests (taiga, formation-type number 7) have an adaptive advantage expressed in higher productivity.
4. In the pine forests of dry environments (curve C) the interaction of moisture and temperature factors (and possibly consequent differences in soil fertility) produces a steeper decrease of net production with elevation.

The manner in which these relations are to be extended to the tropics is not yet established. Apparently, however, the fraction of gross productivity that is expended in plant respiration increases from 50 to 60 per cent in most temperate forests to around 75 per cent in tropical forests. It seems likely that net productions of many climax tropical forests do not much exceed those of temperate forests of favorable environments. The gross productivity of climax tropical forests should be considerably higher, and both gross and net productivity may be very high in successional forests in the tropics.

Within a given climate productivity may be affected by differences of soil fertility. Such effects are well known in agricultural crops, little studied as yet in natural vegetation. There is a general tendency for productivity to increase through the course of succession, but exceptions occur. In a secondary succession on an abandoned farm field, the weeds may have higher production during the first summer, using freely available nutrients, than during following summers. As the succession proceeds, however, the community develops a forest structure, which more effectively uses soil and aboveground space and has a higher stock of circulating nutrients. Productivity thus increases from the weed through the grass and shrub stages to the forest climax as illustrated in Figure 4·3. In many forest successions, in contrast with Figure 4·3, productivity decreases from a maximum in a stage before the climax into the climax itself. Unstable and successional communities can have very high productions.

Climax status is thus not defined by maximum productivity. Climax

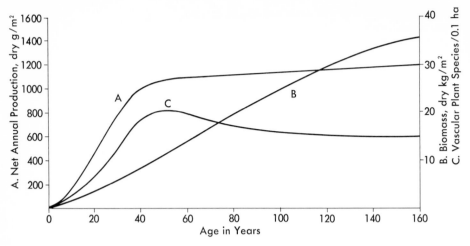

Figure 4·3. Production and biomass in forest succession following fire on Long Island, New York. Production **(A)** increased rapidly through herb and shrub stages to a forest with a stable production around 1,050 g/m²/yr aboveground in the period forty to fifty-five years after the fire. Biomass **(B)** was still increasing in this period and would be expected to reach a stable level near 40 kg/m² in a mature oak forest by about two hundred years after the fire. Species diversity **(C)** is highest in an early forest stage in which some of the successional species are still present, apparently lower in older forests in this area. [Data of Whittaker and Woodwell, 1968, 1969.]

status represents, rather, a steady-state balance of community productivity and decomposition, of photosynthesis and respiration. In the successional community, productivity will normally exceed respiration, and the difference accumulates as biomass increases in the community. The ratio of total respiration to gross productivity is an expression of the extent to which the community is in a successional state with still-increasing biomass. This ratio is 0.80, for example, in the successional oak-pine forest of Figure 4·3 and Table 4·1 at forty-seven years after a fire. The ratio should, of course, approach 1.0 in the climax condition. The word *approach* here expresses the belief that in some communities sufficiently stabilized to be regarded as climax there may still be gradual accumulation of a small organic-matter profit in the soil or in the form of peat. Fossil fuels, coal and petroleum, represent such profit accumulated in past geological time. Although productivity may not be maximum in the climax, for a given succession the biomass and biomass accumulation ratio will normally be maximum in the climax. (The biomass accumulation ratio is not effectively related to the ratio of respiration to production and is more an expression of age and size of dominant plants than of successional status as such.)

The suggested productivity for many temperate-zone forests, 1,200 to 1,500 g/m²/yr net and 2,500 to 3,500 g/m²/yr gross, is a convenient reference range or norm for terrestrial productivities. Productivities of most terrestrial communities fall below this range because of limitations of water, temperature, or soil nutrients, or because of their early successional status. Certain communities have higher productions, however; among them are some rainforests, marshes, successional communities in favorable environments, and some of man's communities of intensive cultivation, notably sugar cane and rice. These communities all have their reasons for especially high productivity, for they occur in environments that in different ways combine high moisture availability, relatively warm temperature, and continuing nutrient replenishment.

The high productivities of these communities have equivocal meaning in relation to human problems. They suggest on the one hand that appropriate techniques, supplying adequate water and nutrients, could produce very high yields in most land environments without the need to modify natural conditions of light, temperature, and CO_2 level. It is possible in theory to increase very much the productivity of the land surface for human needs. The limited occurrence of very high productivities implies on the other hand that these require special circumstances that escape the normal restrictions on terrestrial production. Only by substantial technological effort and expense, involving irrigation, or continuing nutrient addition, or both, applied to particular crop strains of favorable characteristics, with control of loss to pests, are the high yields realized in agriculture. The best lands are now under intensive cultivation; for many areas, especially of the Tropics, Far North, mountain slopes, and arid lands, there is either no known technique for productive cultivation, or no present prospect of irrigation. Whole complexes of reasons involving the controls of productivity, limitations of environments and agricultural technology, and political, cultural, and economic circumstances are responsible for the actual limitations on world food production. Hopes based on high yields in favorable circumstances have had a seductive effect in diverting attention from the realities of the difficult, laborious, research-demanding, expense- and organization-requiring, slow effort to increase food harvest for human beings. It is true both that man could feed well a human population stabilized at a realistic level, and that he is failing now to feed adequately a growing world population even at its present level.

Marine Productivity

Because abundant moisture generally implies high productivity on land, one might expect aquatic communities to be highly productive. They are, in many cases, not. The plankton of the open oceans occupies a larger area of the earth's surface than all other kinds of photosynthetic communities together; its productivity is consequently of interest. The photosynthetic plankton or phytoplankton is a thin suspension in the surface waters of the sea. This ecosystem is especially suited to the quantitative treatment of controls on its productivity in an approach developed by Steele and Riley. We may consider relationships affecting productivity in the column of water below a square meter of the surface of the open sea.

Only that uppermost part of the column that is illuminated by sunlight counts as an environment of primary productivity. Ocean waters are often highly transparent; visible amounts of sunlight penetrate well below 100 m depth in some seas, especially in the Tropics. The depth of the compensation point—the light intensity at which plant respiration equals photosynthesis—may be used as the lower limit of the productive, lighted, euphotic layer. The light intensity at the compensation point varies with species and physiological state of plants, environmental factors other than light, and span of time considered, but 1 per cent of full sunlight is a conventional approximation. Depth of the productive layer is on this basis between 30 and 120 m in most open ocean waters. A 1 per cent limit of light intensity corresponds to that on the floor of many forests, but terrestrial communities, even forests, are shallower photosynthetic systems than the marine plankton. Depth of light penetration in the open ocean is in large part determined by absorption by the plankton itself; more correctly it is determined by absorption by the seston—plankton plus dead organic particles in the water—as well as by the water itself. Depth of light penetration is consequently inversely related to productivity. Depth of light penetration decreases from tropical open oceans to temperate open oceans and from these to inshore waters in which both high plankton production and particles derived from other sources limit light penetration. (The depth may be estimated from the relation of the extinction coefficient, k, to depth in meters, L, of a limiting light intensity, I_d, below a surface sunlight intensity, I_o, through water with a chlorophyll content, C_h, of the seston in μg/liter of water. The extinction equation and some observed relationships of k, C_h, and L are $I_d = I_o e^{-kL}$, $k = 0.04 + 0.0088C_h + 0.054C_h^{2/3}$, hence if $I_d = 0.01 \times I_o$, $L = 4.605/k$.)

Neither on land nor in the sea is photosynthesis simply proportional to light intensity. At lower light intensities, however, photosynthesis approaches a direct, linear relation to light intensity. Above these low light intensities a point of light saturation occurs beyond which photosynthesis does not increase with increased light intensity, and at still higher light intensities, such as those close to the ocean surface at midday, photosynthesis is inhibited and occurs at lower rates than at intermediate light intensities. For this discussion of the broad relationships of marine plankton production, the complex interrelations of light, chlorophyll, and photosynthesis with depth may be shortcut. We may consider that summer sunlight intensities are of similar magnitudes in temperate and tropical waters, that over-all efficiencies of light use by plankton at all depths are similar in temperate and tropical waters of similar productivities, and that productivity is controlled by factors other than light intensity. The effective factors are, primarily, nutrients.

As described above, the plankton has a problem with sinking. Despite all adaptations, a certain fraction of the plankton organisms and their dead remains must sink below the lighted zone, carrying with them nutrients incorporated in protoplasm and skeletons. The loss of nutrients from the lighted zone is intensified by another phenomenon. The warm waters of the open ocean in the tropics and in the temperate-zone summer are (like those of many lakes in summer) stratified: a layer of warmer and less dense water floats on top of the colder and denser water of the depths, separated by a zone of relatively rapid temperature change per unit depth, the thermocline. Because water density decreases upward in the thermocline, its waters are stable. Vertical movements of water by waves and other forces affect primarily the warm waters above the thermocline. The thermocline is consequently a relative barrier to the return of nutrients from the lower levels to the upper warm and lighted waters. Depth of the warm water above the thermocline, and of the lighted water above the 1 per cent level may correspond roughly, though they will not necessarily do so. But the sinking of plankton implies the depletion to low concentrations of the nutrients in the warm and lighted, productive surface waters, and consequently the low productivity of the open oceans. (The rate of sinking of seston is highly variable with kind and size of organisms and particles, and it increases with warmer water temperature and consequent lower viscosity. Mean rates of sinking, v, ranging from 3 m/day in cooler to 6 m/day in warmer waters, are thought reasonable. The rate of loss of plankton or nutrients by sinking, as a decimal fraction per day, may be expressed as v/L).

Plankton productivity in the stratified open ocean waters does not decline asymptotically to zero in consequence of the loss of nutrients with sinking, however. Despite the relative stability of the thermocline, there is some return of nutrients resulting from turbulent movement of water at and below the lower limit of the lighted zone. Plankton production declines not to zero but to a steady-state level at which loss of nutrients by sinking and return of nutrients by water mixing are in balance. A low mixing rate in stratified water necessarily implies low steady-state production. Production can also be limited, however, by a high mixing rate in unstratified water, in which mixing depletes the photosynthetic plankton by diluting it from the lighted surface water into the underlying dark water. (The mixing rate, m, is the decimal fraction of the productive water displaced downward below the lighted zone (and consequently replaced by nutrient-bearing water from below) per unit time. Mixing rates between 0.02/day and 0.05/day support maximum plankton production; mixing rates one or two orders of magnitude less, 0.005 to 0.0005/day, are normal in the stratified open ocean. For production calculations the effect may be expressed as $m(p_o - p)$, the mixing rate times the difference between nutrient concentration of the dark water, p_o, and of the lighted water, p, both in μg/liter. At steady state $pv/L = m(p_o - p)$.)

Steady-state nutrient levels thus determine the rate of productivity in the stratified open ocean. Because the critical nutrient elements are taken up by plankton until only very low concentrations remain in the water, these concentrations themselves do not simply determine productivity. The effective relationship is that between the rate at which nutrients become available and the rate of productivity. The rate at which nutrients become available depends strongly on mixing, but also partly on the rate of nutrient circulation in the plankton ecosystem itself—the rate at which the nutrient leaves phytoplankton cells and becomes available for new uptake by phytoplankton cells. There are a number of routes for this circulation—direct loss from phytoplankton cells into water, death and decomposition of the cells, and grazing by animals followed by excretion or by death and decomposition. Grazing and excretion by animals may be most significant in the plankton and the role of bacteria and the fungi of decay less prominent than in terrestrial communities. (Let c be a conversion factor between phytoplankton biomass in grams of carbon per m^3 of water and a given nutrient in μg/liter of water, e an excretion rate as a decimal fraction of the nutrients taken up by grazing animals, g a grazing rate in liters of water from which phytoplankton are harvested per day by a unit biomass (one gram of carbon per cubic meter of water) of plankton herbivores, h the biomass of the herbivore population, also in gC/m^3, and P the phytoplankton biomass in gC/m^3, then the nutrient regeneration within the lighted zone by this route will be, $r = ceghP$. If, for example, with phosphorus as a nutrient present at low concentrations in the water $c = 0.774$, and if $e = 0.85$ and $g = 3.4$, then $r = 2.2hP$. The rate of change of h may be expressed as $dh/dt = h(gP - r_h - fC)$, in which r_h is the respiratory rate of the herbivores, and f is a feeding coefficient as a decimal fraction of herbivore biomass harvested per unit biomass of carnivores, C. Estimates of the steady-state relations of herbivore to phytoplankton biomass, h/P, range from near equality in some conditions with low feeding rates of carnivores, $f = 0.0025$, to one third or one half with higher feeding rates of the order of $f = 0.01$.)

There is evidence that phosphorus is the most critical nutrient element in many open ocean waters; other elements, including nitrogen that is available in soluble compounds, tend either to be present in less critically short supply, or to parallel phosphorus in their depletion from the lighted zone. A first estimate of open ocean production may consequently be based on phosphate relations in the plankton ecosystem. At low levels of phosphate in the water, the rate of photosynthesis is directly related to phosphate concentration in the water. (The phytoplankton growth rate may be designated P_r, the decimal fraction of its biomass that the plankton produces per day as net primary production. For phosphate levels between 0.05 and 0.40, P_r may be estimated as 0.66 times the value of p in μg/liter. Equations describing phytoplankton production for the open sea in a simplified, approximate, but reasonable way are

$dP/dt = P(P_r - gh - v/L - m)$, change in phytoplankton biomass, P, equals production minus grazing minus sinking minus downward mixing of phytoplankton cells, and

$dp/dt = cP(egh - P_r) + m(p_o - p)$, change in phosphorus level, p, in the water equals release by recycling minus uptake in production plus net return in mixing. For the latter, in steady state,

$cPP_r = ceghP + m(p_o - p)$.

The rate of incorporation of phosphorus in phytoplankton production equals the sum of the rates of recycling of phosphorus through herbivores, $ceghP$, and of phosphorus return by mixing from the water below the lighted zone, $m(p_o - p)$. PP_r is the desired phytoplankton net production in grams of carbon per unit m^3 of water per day.)

(The calculations cannot be described further (see Riley 1965). As an example, for the area of the North Sea studied by Steele in summer, with a mean mixing coefficient of 0.0042, $p_o = 0.7$ μg/liter, and estimated chlorophyll content of 0.84 μg/liter (compared with a mean observed value of 0.77), calculations give a mean phosphate concentration in the lighted zone, $p = 0.265$, and the corresponding $P_r = 0.175$, and phytoplankton biomass $P = 0.030$ gC/m^3. Estimated phytoplankton production summed for the 37 m. column of lighted water is 0.26 grams of carbon below a square meter of the ocean surface per day.) Compared with the estimated production of 0.26 grams of carbon per meter square of the ocean surface per day in an area of the North Sea, an independent measurement by the ^{14}C technique averaged 0.29 gC/m^2/day. An approximate conversion factor of 2.5 from grams of carbon to dry grams of organic matter in net production gives 0.72 dry g/m^2/day. Production estimates and measurements in most tropical open oceans in summer are lower, of the order of 0.05 to 0.20 gC/m^2/day.

Yearly cycles of production in temperate open seas include winter periods of reduced light intensity and productivity, and spring periods of increased mixing and higher productivity. Many tropical areas also have periods of higher mixing rates. An estimated mean annual net production for open waters of the North Sea area is 68 gC/m²/yr, or 170 dry g/m²/yr. A comparable value for the Sargasso Sea is 72 gC/m²/yr or 180 dry g/m²/yr, values for other tropic open oceans outside up-welling areas are 40 to 120 dry g/m²/yr. Temperature has complex and conflicting effects on open ocean production. The increased strati-fication and sinking rates that go with higher temperatures act to re-duce productivity in the Tropics, whereas the low winter light intensi-ties correlated with low temperatures act to reduce productivity in the Temperate Zone. The effect of temperature on metabolic rates and rate of feeding of plankton herbivores is not a strong one, because organisms of different climatic belts and seasons are adapted to effec-tive function in the temperatures of their environments. Similar year-round productivities may result from lower production rates by smaller plankton biomass in a deeper lighted column through a longer warm season in the Tropics, and higher summer production in a shallower lighted layer combined with low winter production in the Temperate Zone.

Because of the difficulties of the radiocarbon method, estimates of marine production may be subject to revision toward higher values. It is easy, however, to characterize communities that would be sup-ported by net productions of 40 to 180 dry g/m²/yr on land: desert. As the northern continents and Australia have arid interiors of low productivity, so the oceans have nutrient-poor "interiors" of low pro-ductivity. Where upwelling—movement of cold, nutrient-rich water from the depths to the surface of the ocean—occurs, productivity is higher. Upwelling occurs (a) in an area surrounding the Antarctic continent, (b) in certain arctic areas of the North Atlantic and west-ern North Pacific, (c) near the equator in the Pacific Ocean, and (d) along the western sides of continents where a current flowing toward the equator tends (because of the Coriolis force) to curve away from the shore, drawing water upward from the depths near the shore. With or without upwelling, productivity is in general higher in the shallower waters on the continental shelves. The reasons that the in-shore waters are more productive (although their lighted layer is less deep) include more effective turnover of nutrients from deeper waters and bottom sediments to the lighted layer, drainage of nutrients into the sea by rivers and estuaries, and the contribution of attached sea-weeds to production.

Plankton production on the continental shelves is in general between 200 and 600 dry g/m²/yr, but ranges upward toward 1,000 g/m²/yr in some areas of upwelling. Productions in estuaries are high—near 1,000 g/m²/yr in measurements in Long Island Sound. In some in-shore waters high productions by attached algae and eelgrass are added to plankton productions. The giant kelp beds of the California coast have some of the highest productions known for any ecosystem; tropical coral reefs also are among the most productive of ecosystems. In both these cases the productivity is supported by nutrients carried past the organisms by moving water; in both cases some fraction of the measured productivity is probably secondary or heterotrophic (based on use of organic matter in the water) rather than primary or autotrophic. Marine productivities cover the same wide range of values as terrestrial productivities—from values corresponding to most arid deserts (less than 2 dry $g/m^2/yr$ in the weak light beneath the Arctic ice cap) to values well above 3,000 dry $g/m^2/yr$ in some communities of especially favorable circumstances. Fresh-water ecosystems show a correspondingly wide range of production values. The highest productivities occur on the margins of the land and water—certain hydric communities on land, and certain inshore and shallow communities in water.

The highly productive marine waters are essentially the fringes of the oceans. The major commercial fisheries of the world depend on the harvest of these fringes. The fish harvested are carnivores of high positions in food chains. For reasons to be explained in a following section man can harvest through these carnivores small fractions— much below 1 per cent—of net primary production. Direct harvest of marine plankton by ships and nets is exorbitantly costly, and extensive underwater "farming" on the continental shelves does not yet appear economically or technologically feasible. No technique for more successful harvest of marine production of food than that through marine animals is yet in prospect. A large share of the most productive marine fish populations are already being harvested; only limited increase in harvest, probably less than a doubling of the present catch, seems likely. Reductions in the harvest of some marine populations must be expected because of the effects of pollution, excessive harvest, and destruction of breeding areas in estuaries. The giant kelp beds of the southern California coast have been reduced to as little as one tenth of their former area by pollution affecting both the kelp and sea urchins that feed on their bases. The California sardines were overfished to the extinction of the industry dependent on them, and the whales of the world are being overharvested toward extinction. The oceans are great and taken as wholes greatly productive, but the idea that they offer abundances of food awaiting harvest to feed hungry nations is an illusion.

Pyramids and Efficiencies

Three major ways (or groups of ways) in which aquatic animals obtain food have been mentioned: (1) The filtering from the water of the living particles of plankton by plankton animals. A large part of this filtering in the sea is done by copepods (Figure 1·1), microcrustaceans (mostly 0.5 to 8 mm. long) with appendages adapted as miniature rakes or combs that strain particles from the water. Such a straining process is largely unselective except for the size of particles. What the copepod collects with its rake is consequently seston, a mixed harvest of living cells and dead cells and fragments. Despite the apparent indiscriminateness of this process, there is room for niche differentiation in behavior and in the size and kind of particles eaten among these animals. (2) The nutrient rain of seston particles that settles through the water toward the depths of the water body. Some of these particles feed plankton organisms of the unlighted deeper water; others feed bottom organisms with ciliated tentacles, water tubes, and other techniques for the concentration of organic material from water. In the bottom community, the benthos, there is again a wide range of techniques of nutrition, one aspect of an impressive diversity of species, forms of organisms, and animal phyla. (3) Aquatic animals that are, like many terrestrial ones, predators that capture and feed upon other animals.

Diatoms, plant plankton cells, may be raked from the water and eaten by copepods. Small fish, sardines, say, eat the copepods. These sardines are eaten by larger fish, and these in turn are eaten by still larger predatory fish—such as tuna or shark. An atom of organic carbon may by this time be incorporated in the protoplasm of a fifth organism in the sequence from diatom to shark. A shorter sequence may lead from phytoplankton to a larger crustacean plankter (krill or euphausiid shrimp) to one of the baleen whales that feeds by straining these crustaceans out of the water.

Such sequences represent the familiar idea of food chains. Numbers of links in such chains are variable, but three to five links are common. Positions of links in the chains are named

1. Producer, the photosynthetic plant or first organism of the sequence.
2. Herbivore or primary consumer, the first animal, which feeds on plant food.
3. First carnivore or secondary consumer, an animal feeding (as predator, parasite, or scavenger) on a plant-eating animal.
4. Secondary carnivore or tertiary consumer, feeding on the preceding.
5. Tertiary carnivore.

These positions along food chains are *trophic levels* and are useful for studying community food relations even though the boundaries of the levels are not sharp. Many animals take any food that is suitable in size range and other characteristics, and consequently they take food from more than one trophic level.

Productivity of the animal plankton is less than that of the plant plankton. Such must be the case for more than one reason: only the fraction of primary production that is net, remaining after plant respiration, can be harvested. Of this net primary production only a fraction can be harvested live by animals, if they are not by overharvest to destroy their own food sources. Only part of the plant material eaten by animals will be digested and assimilated. For most animals, both the silicious walls of diatoms and the cellulose walls of land plants are useless as food even though the latter are organic material. For these reasons production of the second trophic level, the herbivorous animals, is generally one tenth or less that of the plants on the first level. For similar reasons production of the first carnivores must be less than that of the herbivores, and production of the secondary carnivores must be less than that of the first carnivores.

There must be a steep, stepwise decrease in production up the sequence of trophic levels, which forms the pyramid of productivity (Figure 4·4A). Two other pyramids appear as corollaries. The num-

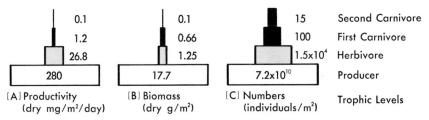

	0.1	0.1	15	Second Carnivore
	1.2	0.66	100	First Carnivore
	26.8	1.25	1.5×10^4	Herbivore
	280	17.7	7.2×10^{10}	Producer
	[A] Productivity (dry mg/m²/day)	[B] Biomass (dry g/m²)	[C] Numbers (individuals/m²)	Trophic Levels

Figure 4·4. Community pyramids for a shallow experimental pond of low nutrient content. [Data of Whittaker, 1961.] Productivity was estimated from rate of phosphorus uptake; the fourth trophic level was estimated as a fraction of carnivores feeding on both the second and third levels. Widths of steps for numbers of organisms are on a logarithmic scale.

bers of individual organisms will generally decrease up the sequence of levels to form the pyramid of numbers (Figure 4·4C). Pyramids of numbers, however, are subject to reversal when many small organisms feed on one large organism of a lower level, as thousands of insects may feed on a tree, or hundreds of parasitic worms on one host. Biomasses for trophic levels also decrease up the sequence (Figure 4·4B). Biomass pyramids are less frequently reversed, but animals at times exceed plants in mass in plankton communities. It is the pyramid of productivity that has fundamental significance; the pyramids of numbers and biomass are less fundamental and less reliable consequences of it.

A ratio of a level of the pyramid of productivity to the preceding level is an efficiency. The first efficiency of interest is the relation of the productivity of the first trophic level to the energy of sunlight, which supports it. In the North Sea plankton community, the energy of incident sunlight in the visible range at the ocean surface in summer is about 0.329 cal/cm^2/min or 473 cal/cm^2/day. Part of this light is reflected by and absorbed in the water. Only the light that reaches plant cells can be used by the phytoplankton for photosynthesis. Only that fraction of the visible spectrum that plant pigments can absorb, and only that fraction of this that is actually absorbed and made available to the photosynthetic process, can result in productivity. The efficiency of photosynthesis is necessarily low. In the North Sea plankton community, a net productivity of 0.72 g/m^2/day converts to energy of 0.306 cal/cm^2/day, and this relative to incident sunlight in the visible spectrum is an efficiency of only 0.065 per cent.

In a forest, foliage of different plants is staged in depth as has been described. Above a square meter of a deciduous forest floor there are a leaf) containing about 2 g. of chlorophyll (Table 4·1). There is an 4 to 6 square meters of surfaces of leaves (counting only one surface of additional 1.5 to 2.0 m^2 of bark surface (computing this as if the bark were smooth). Leaf and bark surface together often extinguish the light to and beyond the compensation point. In many forests, light intensity on the forest floor is 1 to 2 per cent of incident sunlight at midday; in some forests it is around 0.2 per cent. Efficiencies in relation to light and the forest's light-receiving structure can be expressed in several ways. A net primary productivity of 1,200 g/m^2/yr in the oak-pine forest is equivalent to 510 cal/cm^2/yr; in relation to an annual sunlight energy of the visible spectrum of 56,000 cal/cm^2/yr the net production efficiency is 0.91 per cent. The corresponding efficiency of gross productivity in relation to year-around incident sunlight in the visible range is 2.0 per cent. A gross productivity of 2,650 g/m^2/yr implies also annual photosynthetic capture of 3,000 kCal energy per square meter of leaf surface, for productive output of 700 dry g/m^2 of leaf surface, and 1,400 dry g/g of chlorophyll.

The net production efficiencies of 0.91 per cent and 0.065 per cent are representative values for ecosystems of moderately high and relatively low productivities. Because of the wide expanses of open ocean and the extent of arid and cold desert on land, the mean for the earth's surface is heavily weighted toward the lower end. The estimated mean productivity for the earth's surface (Table 4·2) implies, with a mean sunlight energy of about 55,000 cal/cm^2/yr, an overall efficiency of world net production of 0.25 per cent. The corresponding value for efficiency of gross production should be around twice this value.

Efficiencies of the second trophic level in relation to the first can be variously expressed, using either the gross or the net production of the producers, and for the second level combinations of respiration, yield (as loss from the trophic level by predator harvest, death, and removal or emigration), excretion, and dry weight growth of herbivorous animals, or of these plus the bacteria and fungi feeding on plant material. One appropriate expression of efficiency of the second trophic level compares herbivore production as respiration plus yield (including excretion with this) with gross photosynthesis, and gives efficiency values ranging from about 10 per cent down. Efficiencies of the third level, comparing respiration and yield for primary carnivores and herbivores, can (but will not necessarily) be somewhat higher: values may range from 15 per cent down. Efficiency of food utilization by a carnivore can be higher than that of an herbivore because of the closer match of the carnivore's food to its own chemical composition and needs.

There is thus a tendency for efficiencies relating a trophic level to the preceding level to increase up the pyramid: from green plants to herbivores and (in some cases) from herbivores to carnivores. Efficiencies related to human harvest should be differently stated. What man takes is not productivity as such, but a yield—a fraction of productivity that it is feasible to remove and utilize without destroying the basis of the productivity. Efficiency of human harvest is most appropriately stated as dry mass of yield, relative to dry mass of net primary production, per unit area and time. Man can harvest around 30 per cent of net primary production when plant material is taken as either the grain of cereal crops or the wood from a forest. Higher efficiencies are possible in some favorable circumstances, but lower ones apply to many environments and crop species. If harvest is in the form of the meat of herbivorous animals, the harvest efficiency must be lower than the trophic-level efficiency, hence less than 10 per cent. Pyramid relations imply that if the meat of aquatic carnivores is used, the harvest efficiencies in relation to primary production will range downward from 1.0, 0.1, and 0.01 per cent for primary, secondary, and tertiary carnivores respectively. For harvest of animal populations also, yield is a figure different from, and lower than, productivity. Only a fraction of a population can be harvested on a sustained basis—that fraction that represents a surplus above the individuals necessary to maintain the reproduction and growth of the population itself. This limitation on harvest is one of the factors determining trophic level efficiencies, and when man's harvest exceeds this limitation, decline in productivity and yield may result—as observed in overfishing and overgrazing.

Reducers

Production and efficiencies have so far been discussed as if only two major groups of organisms were involved—green plants (producers), and animals (consumers). The roles of these in communities are clearly different; the producers use the energy of sunlight to create food, and the consumers harvest and eat part of this food. The fact that they harvest only a part of the community's production indicates the significance of a third major group of organisms, which utilizes the remainder. Organisms of the third group are the reducers or decomposers—the saprobes or organisms of decomposition and decay, the bacteria and fungi. These organisms live on or within organic food supplies, especially dead tissues, and feed by absorption of soluble organic food; in many cases digestive enzymes are excreted from the bacterial cells or fungal hyphae to digest organic matter into the soluble form that is absorbed. Through such digestion and the effects of their own respiration, the reducers break down organic matter to inorganic remnants, in the process utilizing organic energy not harvested by the consumers and releasing inorganic nutrients back into the environment.

The reducers are the least visible of the three fractions of the community. Bacteria are part of the plankton, and some lower fungi (chytrids) occur, but these are inconspicuous. The few mushrooms that may be seen on a forest floor scarcely suggest the rich saprobic life of the soil, which includes many kinds of bacteria and fungi of diverse nutritive relations to living and dead plant roots, leaf litter and soil organic matter, dead stem and branch wood, and other food sources. Reduction of the forest floor litter—fallen dead leaves and stem and branch wood—to soil organic matter and this in turn to inorganic end products is based on the activities of these organisms, together with certain animals. Earthworms feed on dead leaves and on soil organic matter, and termites, in warm climates, on dead wood. Other soil animals and the cryptozoa of the litter and surface soil layers—springtails, mites, millepedes, and so on—feed upon this organic material or primarily on the bacteria or fungi in it. Reducers may thus appear in food chains: plant tissues (death)—earthworm (death)—bacteria of decay. Plant tissues (death)—fungus—springtail—predatory mite (death)—bacteria of decay. Food chains may or may not include top carnivores, but they may include, and will normally end with, reducers. In most communities any dead organic matter, whether of a plant, an animal, or a saprobe, is finally decomposed by saprobes to inorganic matter.

There are not two major groups of organisms in natural communities—plants and animals—but three—plants, animals, and saprobes. These three (though parasites occur in all three) correspond in general to the producers, consumers, and reducers that are the functional kingdoms of natural communities. The three represent major directions of evolution and in each, the kinds of organization evolved are closely related to the mode of nutrition. Plants feed primarily by photosynthesis, and the higher forms have evolved toward organizations that include leaves or blades as organs of photosynthesis, supported by stems or stipes, rising from roots or holdfasts that provide anchorage and (in vascular plants) water and nutrient uptake, while the vascular tissues serve for transport between these organs. Animals feed primarily by ingesting food that is digested in and absorbed from an internal cavity. Their organization has consequently evolved toward differentiation of both a digestive tract together with supporting circulatory and excretory systems, and the sensory, nervous, and muscular-and-skeletal systems that permit motility and response to food. Saprobes feed by absorption and have need for an extensive surface of absorption but (apart from reproductive systems) little need for other structural differentiation. The principal kinds of organization evolved among saprobes are the unicellular of bacteria and yeasts, the chytrid of the lower fungi, and in higher fungi the mycelial, with a network of syncytial protoplasmic tubes or hyphae.

The functional kingdoms of communities are not to be identified with the kingdoms of systematics but are a large part of the evolutionary basis of the latter. In the traditional two-kingdom system the animal kingdom includes organisms, both unicellular and multicellular, characterized by ingestion and motility, and the extended plant kingdom includes the primarily photosynthetic groups and (somewhat arbitrarily grouped with them) the predominantly absorptive bacteria and fungi. In current alternatives the bacteria (with the blue-green algae) become the kingdom Monera, characterized by procaryotic organization, whereas the higher plants and animals become kingdoms characterized by the directions of evolution stated above. It is logical to recognize the higher fungi as a kingdom coordinate with these, whereas the eucaryotic unicellular organisms become the kingdom Protista. In the system of Copeland, however, the higher fungi (and the multicellular algae) are retained with the unicells in a broadly defined kingdom of eucaryotic organisms without advanced tissue differentiation, the Protoctista.

In terrestrial communities, as much as 90 per cent of net primary production remains unharvested as living plant tissue and must be utilized as dead tissue by saprobes and soil animals. In terrestrial communities the saprobes have a larger and more essential role than animals in breaking down dead tissues to inorganic matter. In most terrestrial communities secondary production by reducers should exceed that by consumers, though the former is even more difficult to measure than the latter. Biomass of the reducers, with their microscopic cells and filaments embedded in food sources, is also difficult to measure. Biomass of the reducers is small, however, in relation to their productivity and significance for the community. These organisms function as the enzymes of the community: small masses of reducers (with high production consequent on rapid growth and reproduction balanced with mortality) transform far larger masses of organic matter through sequences of reactions to inorganic remnants.

In so doing the reducers disperse back to the environment the energy of photosynthesis in the organic compounds they decompose. They have thus a major part in one of the most general characteristics of ecosystems—energy flow. The manner of the flow is illustrated in a simplified and generalized way in Figure 4·5. A community, like an

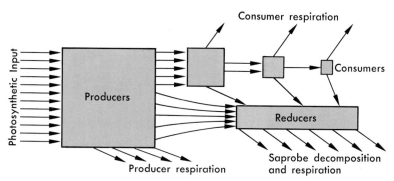

Figure 4·5. Flow of energy in a natural community. In a steady-state community the intake of photosynthetic energy on the left, and the dissipation of energy back to environment toward the right, are in balance; and the pool of energy of organic compounds within the community remains constant.

organism, is an open energy system. Through the continuing intake of energy by photosynthesis the energy dissipated to environment by respiration and biological activity is replaced, and the system does not run down, through the loss of free energy, to maximum entropy. If energy intake exceeds energy dissipation, the pool of biologically useful energy of organic bonds in the community increases as does community biomass, and the community grows; such is the case in succession. If energy loss exceeds intake the community must in some sense retrogress. If energy intake and dissipation are in balance, the pool of organic energy is in a steady state, such as is characteristic of climax communities.

Three aspects of this steady state may be recognized. There are, first, the steady states of the populations of the climax community, in which, with birth and death rates in balance, the population pool or number of individuals remains relatively constant. There is, second, the steady state of energy flow. Third, there is the steady state of the matter of the community, with the addition of material to the community by photosynthesis and organic syntheses balanced against the loss of material by respiration and decomposition. With input and output thus in balance the community itself, with its complexly structured mass of living and dead material, can remain relatively constant. By virtue of its continuing replacement balanced with its losses—of individual organisms, of energy, and of materials—the climax community is potentially immortal if undisturbed.

The reducers have a crucial role in the second most general characteristic of ecosystems—the circulation of materials between community and environment. The manner in which the three functional kingdoms relate to this circulation is indicated in a most generalized form in Figure 4·6. Decomposition of organic matter by reducers releases

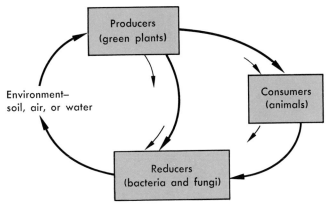

Figure 4·6. **Circulation of materials between environment and organisms in an ecosystem, in simplified form.**

inorganic materials, including nutrients, into the environment—the soil, or the water—from which they may be taken up by plants and recycled through the community. It is the reducers that make possible the closure of the nutrient circuits and the continuing productivity at a relatively high level based on this circulation. The significance of circulation of materials in ecosystems has been touched on in the discussion of plankton production and will be considered further in the following chapter.

Summary

Perhaps the most fundamental dimension of an ecosystem is its productivity—the rate of creation of organic material, by photosynthesis primarily, per unit of area and time. The structure of the community, that is, the vertical disposition of photosynthetic cells, or leaves, of different species, is adapted to the interception and utilization of light of different intensities in photosynthesis. All biological activity of the community, and of human life, is dependent on the energy of gross primary productivity, the energy bound in photosynthesis. The amounts of this productivity are controlled by a number of characteristics of environment, notably nutrient availability, water availability (on land), and temperature; high productivities result from favorable combinations of these characteristics. Large areas of the continents are deserts of low production because of climatic drought or extreme coldness; even larger areas of the oceans are "deserts" of low production because of the deficiency of nutrients in the surface waters of the open oceans. For varied reasons the efficiencies of utilization of sunlight in the visible range in photosynthesis are not high—for the world as a whole this efficiency of gross primary productivity is around 0.5 per cent. Although over-all productivity of the world is very large—of the order of 164 billion metric tons of dry organic matter net production per year—effective limitations on what man harvests as food result from characteristics of environment that affect production, ecosystem function and harvest efficiencies, and harvest technology and economic and cultural factors.

Three major modes of nutrition and ways of utilizing productivity are represented in the three functional kingdoms of natural communities—the producers, or green plants that create their own food and respire part of it for their needs; the consumers, or animals that feed by ingestion and internal digestion of organic material; and the reducers, or bacteria and fungi, which live by absorptive nutrition, employing external digestion and decomposing organic matter to inorganic products. That part of gross primary productivity that is not respired by green plants is net primary productivity and is available for harvest by consumers and reducers. Organic material and energy are passed along food chains—from plants, through first consumers (or first reducers), to second and third consumers (or reducers). The steps along food chains, when organisms are grouped by their positions in food chains, are trophic levels.

Because energy is dissipated in respiration on each trophic level, there must be a step-wise decrease in productivity, a pyramid relationship through the sequence of trophic levels. If net primary productivity is rapidly used by consumers, the community may have only a small biomass of organic material accumulated in its plants, as in the plankton. If harvest is mostly delayed, extensive biomass may accumulate in a complex vegetation structure, as in forests. If the rate at which organic matter is produced exceeds that at which it is decomposed, the biomass and structure of the community increase, as in succession. If the rates of photosynthesis and respiration, production and decomposition, are in balance, the community is in a steady state, as is the case in climax communities. Maintenance of a relatively high level of production in this steady state is dependent on the consumers and reducers, which by utilization of plant food and decomposition release inorganic nutrients for new uptake by plants, and thus make possible the continuing circulation of nutrients through the ecosystem.

References

Eckardt, F. E., editor. (1968) *Functioning of Terrestrial Ecosystems at the Primary Production Level.* (symposium) Paris: Unesco. 516 pp.

Goldman, Charles R., editor. (1966) *Primary Productivity in Aquatic Environments.* (symposium) Berkeley and Los Angeles: University of California Press. 464 pp.

Odum, Eugene P., and H. T. Odum. (1959) *Fundamentals of Ecology,* 2nd ed. Philadelphia and London: Saunders. xvii + 546 pp.

Phillipson, John. (1966) *Ecological Energetics.* London: Arnold. 57 pp.

Rodin, L. E., and N. I. Bazilevich. (1968) *Production and Mineral Cycling in Terrestrial Vegetation.* Transl. ed. by G. E. Fogg. Edinburgh: Oliver & Boyd. v + 288 pp.

Turner, Frederick B., editor. (1968) "Energy flow and ecological systems" (symposium). *American Zoologist,* **8**:10–69.

Brown, L. R. (1967) "The world outlook for conventional agriculture." *Science,* **158**:604–611.

Engelmann, M. D. (1966) "Energetics, terrestrial field studies, and animal productivity." *Advances in Ecological Research,* **3**:73–115.

Lindeman, R. L. (1942) "The trophic-dynamic aspect of ecology." *Ecology,* **23**:399–418.

Odum, H. T. (1956) "Primary production in flowing waters." *Limnology and Oceanography,* **1**:102–117.

Ovington, J. D. (1962) "Quantitative ecology and the woodland ecosystem concept." *Advances in Ecological Research,* **1**:103–192.

Raymont, J. E. G. (1966) "The production of marine plankton." *Advances in Ecological Research,* **3**:117–205.

Riley, G. A. (1965) "A mathematical model of regional variations in plankton." *Limnology and Oceanography,* **10**(Suppl):R202–R205.

Ryther, J. H. (1963) "Geographic variations in productivity." In *The Sea,* M. N. Hill, editor. London: Interscience. Vol. **2**, pp. 347–380.

Slobodkin, L. B. (1962) "Energy in animal ecology." *Advances in Ecological Research,* **1**:69–101.

Steele, J. H. (1958) "Plant production in the northern North Sea." *Marine Research, Scientific Home Department,* 1958(**7**):1–36.

Steemann Nielsen, E. (1963) "Productivity, definition and measurement." In *The Sea,* M. N. Hill, editor. London: Interscience. Vol. **2**, pp. 129–164.

Strickland, J. D. H. (1965) "Production of organic matter in the primary stages of the marine food chain." In *Chemical Oceanography*, J. P. Riley and G. Skirrow, editors. London and New York: Academic Press. Vol. **1**, pp. 477–610.

Westlake, D. F. (1963) "Comparisons of plant productivity." *Biological Reviews*, **38**:385–425.

Whittaker, R. H. (1966) "Forest dimensions and production in the Great Smoky Mountains." *Ecology*, **47**:103–121.

Whittaker, R. H. (1969) "New concepts of kingdoms of organisms." *Science*, **163**:150–160.

Whittaker, R. H., and G. M. Woodwell. (1968) "Dimension and production relations of trees and shrubs in the Brookhaven Forest, New York." *Journal of Ecology*, **56**:1–25.

Whittaker, R. H., and G. M. Woodwell. (1969) "Structure, production and diversity of the oak-pine forest at Brookhaven, New York." *Journal of Ecology*, **57**:157–176.

Cycling and Pollution

Phosphorus in an Aquarium

CIRCULATION OF MATERIALS through cycles involving producers, consumers, and reducers is, along with flow of energy, a general phenomenon of communities and ecosystems. The processes of transfer and concentration of materials in ecosystems have also great, and increasingly urgent, significance to man. We can illustrate with certain studies some of the principles from which their importance to man results.

Phosphorus has a major role in determining productivity of plankton communities. It is natural that, for further study of the role of phosphorus in aquatic communities, radiophosphorus (^{32}P) should be introduced and followed as a community-level tracer. Such experiments can well be done in the laboratory, using either a plankton-and-water sample from a natural aquatic community or the small-scale community that develops through some weeks in an aquarium provided with water and nutrients and an initial seeding with pond organisms. Into a 200-liter aquarium microcosm of the latter sort 100 μc of ^{32}P-labeled phosphate (as phosphoric acid) were introduced, with results shown in Figure 5·1. After the tracer introduction

(1) There was initial, very rapid movement from water into plankton organisms and turnover from these back to water. In the experiment illustrated one half of the ^{32}P had moved into the plankton (predominantly single-celled green algae) within two hours, and by twelve hours the distribution of ^{32}P was in a steady-state balance between plankton and water. Other experiments, using millipore filters for fuller separation of small plankton cells and particles with bacteria

105

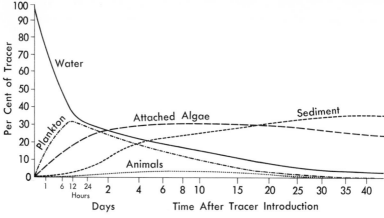

Figure 5·1. Movement of radiophosphorus in an aquarium microcosm. Percentage of the tracer present at a given time (after correction for radioactive decay) is on the vertical axis, time after tracer introduction (on a square-root scale) on the horizontal. [Whittaker, 1961.]

have shown even faster uptake (up to half the amount in the water in three minutes) and balance (93 per cent in the plankton and particles after twenty minutes). Turnover rates (in fractions of the ^{32}P in the plankton returning to the water per unit time) were 0.27/hr. and 0.013/min. for the two experiments. These rapid movements of ^{32}P are affected by adsorption onto surfaces of cells as well as absorption through those surfaces. The mass of the plankton is very small in relation to the water in which it is suspended. With the greater part of the phosphate in this small mass, the concentration ratios (expressed as ^{32}P content per unit dry mass of organisms divided by ^{32}P content of an equal mass of water) are in some cases, with low phosphate content in the water, of the order of one to two million-fold.

(2) Somewhat more slowly through the first few hours, the ^{32}P moved into the filamentous algae growing on the sides and on the mud-containing bottom trays of the aquarium. Maximum ^{32}P content per unit mass and approximate equilibrium with the water were reached for attached algae within twenty-four hours. (In general, the larger the organism, the larger the mass or pool of phosphate it contains, the lower the turnover rate for this pool, the slower the uptake per unit mass, the later the equilibrium is reached, and the slower the decline from that equilibrium if the experiment is continued long enough for such decline to occur.) As a substantial part of the ^{32}P moved into the attached algae, the ^{32}P in the water-and-plankton together declined. Even though equilibrium of ^{32}P content per unit mass of algae and water was reached during the first day, total content

of ^{32}P in attached algae continued to increase, because of the growth in mass of the algae, until the sixth day. Thereafter the turnover of ^{32}P in the algae implied, as ^{32}P levels in the water declined, net movement of ^{32}P out of the algae.

(3) The tracer moved into animals (water fleas grazing the plankton algae, snails grazing the sidewall algae) more slowly than into their food, at rates that varied with size, food habits, and other characteristics of the animals. From the grazing animals the ^{32}P reached the carnivorous animals (fish feeding on water fleas). Although the rate of uptake decreases along a food chain, the concentration ratios at equilibrium in animals may be very high.

(4) Through the latter part of the experiment an increasing fraction of the tracer moved into the bottom mud, the sediment (of recently settled plankton and animal feces), and the film of microorganisms on the aquarium walls. Some turnover of ^{32}P between these three parts of the ecosystem and the water continued. There was, however, net movement of ^{32}P "downward"—out of the water and active circulation between water and organisms, and into the less active or bound forms of the sediment, mud, and surface films. By gradual accumulation three quarters of the ^{32}P had moved into these pools of less active turnover by the end of the experiment, forty-five days after tracer introduction.

The tracer approach can be applied with substances other than ^{32}P-phosphate, but such work is limited as yet. The ^{32}P transfer patterns are representative in broad features of the ways other substances circulate, but details for other isotopes and compounds necessarily vary. In a number of experiments ^{32}P has been released into the waters of lakes, in which its general pattern of movements parallels those in aquarium microcosms. In lakes, however, transport by water currents may have marked effects on the pattern of ^{32}P movement. From experiments in both lakes and microcosms a number of principles can be stated:

1. Rapidity of movement. Introduced substances may be rapidly turned over between water and organisms and effectively removed from the water into organisms. The rapidity of these processes and their effect on water content emphasizes the responsiveness of organisms and communities to the chemistry of environment, and the significance of their effects on the chemistry of environment.

2. High concentration ratios. Although concentration ratios vary with many factors, many-thousand-fold concentrations from environment into organisms are common. Such high concentration ratios can occur both for essential nutrients like phosphates and for toxic materials.

3. Progressive removal from environment, versus steady state. When

a substance is introduced as a single dose, as in the microcosm experiment described, the introduced substance is first concentrated in the organisms and then moves progressively out of active circulation and into less active or inactive forms. The level of a fertilizer (such as phosphate) introduced as a single dose will decline toward the same steady-state level, determined by the functional characteristics of the ecosystem, as existed before its introduction. When a substance is introduced on a continuing, constant basis, however, this continuing introduction becomes one of the factors determining the steady state for the system. A new pattern of pool contents and transfer rates for the system will develop, based on the new rate of introduction and its relation to the system's new rates of turnover and removal.

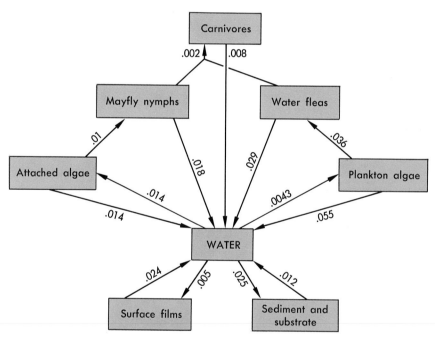

Figure 5·2. A transfer pattern for radiophosphorus in a small outdoor pond. Numbers are transfer rates, as decimal fractions of the ^{32}P in the box at the tail of the arrow, moving into the box at the head of the arrow per hour. [Whittaker, 1961.]

4.   Complexity of transfer pattern. A pattern of ^{32}P movement worked out for an aquarium microcosm is illustrated in Figure 5·2. The diagram is by no means a simple water-plant-animal-water circle, yet the diagram is quite incomplete in relation to the complexity of ^{32}P movements in the pond. Rates and routes of transfer vary in

most diverse ways for different substances in a given ecosystem and can vary for a given substance in different ecosystems.

5. Transfer unity of the ecosystem. A multiplicity of transfers, a complex traffic of many inorganic and organic substances, interrelate organisms with one another and environment and give the ecosystem its functional unity. The pattern of movement of a substance in a large ecosystem is a product of both movements in space (of water, air, and organisms) and movements in place (transfer between organisms and environment and along food chains).

Nutrients in Forests

Some aspects of nutrient cycling are more easily studied in a forest than in a water body. The more complex and massive structure of the forest makes it easier to separate from one another and measure some of the transfer rates for different means of movement and kinds of organisms. In particular, analyses of nutrient element contents of plant tissues may be combined with measurements of biomass and net production of those plant tissues. To these data should be added measurements of nutrient movement into the soil in precipitation, animal harvest of plant tissue and nutrients, and (if possible) information on nutrient release and movement in the soil. Major features of a pattern for nutrient pools and net transfer rates thus obtained are illustrated in Figure 5·3.

To varying degrees the nutrients of a forest ecosystem are concentrated in the tissues of trees: the greater part of the nitrates and phosphates circulating between tree and soil may be in the trees, the greater part of the calcium and sodium in the soil. Circulation of the requisite, but limited, nutrients is relatively tight in the sense that most of the ecosystem's stock of these nutrients is held in the organisms, and the fraction in the soil is subject to rapid turnover between release (as from decaying leaves) and new uptake by roots. When a nutrient is in tight circulation in this sense: (a) the amount present in the soil at a given time is much affected by the turnover rate in the trees, (b) the nutrient may be in sufficiently short supply to affect the productivity of the trees, and (c) an addition of the nutrient to the soil as fertilizer may produce a significant, if temporary, increase in productivity.

Calcium is in loose circulation in many kinds of soils and communities. On soils derived from serpentine rock and peridotite, however, which are low in calcium, it is in tight circulation. Communities on serpentine are often stunted and reduced in structure and productivity compared with those on other adjacent soils, are of markedly different floristic composition, and are dominated by plants adapted to the low calcium levels and other special nutrient conditions on serpentine.

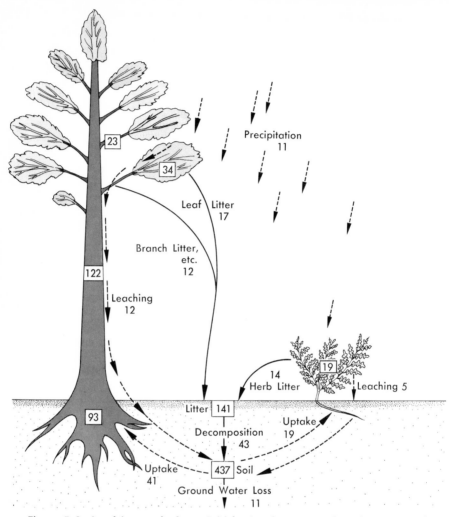

Figure 5·3. A calcium cycle for a British pine forest. Boxed numbers are pools of calcium in kg/ha; unboxed numbers are transfers in kg/ha/yr. The forest and soil are assumed to be in steady state, with a canopy of Scots pine (*Pinus silvestris*) and an undergrowth of bracken fern (*Pteridium aquilinum*). [Pool and transfer values are derived or estimated from Ovington, 1962.]

Many species are represented on serpentine soils by ecotypes distinct from those on other soils. Phosphorus, molybdenum, and zinc are known to be limiting to community production and in tight circulation on certain soils of Australia. Tropical forests apparently have tight nutrient circulation compared with temperate forests. When the forests are cut, as in the shifting agriculture of many tropical areas, the nutrients are rapidly lost by leaching downward in the soil and erosion, and the soil loses its fertility within a few years.

The fall and decay of leaves is the most obvious means of return of nutrients to the soil. There is, however, considerably more to the nutrient return than this. In many plants some fraction of some of the nutrient elements in leaves moves back into woody twig and branch tissues before the leaves fall (while other elements may increase in the leaves up to the time of leaf fall). Plants may thus tend to conserve their supplies of certain nutrients, some of which are in short supply and tight circulation in the forest. In the long range, in the steady-state forest, the woody tissues of stems and branches must also die and decompose and release their nutrients to the soil. In the long range the total uptake from the soil and total return to the soil should be in balance.

The return is further affected by leaching from plant surfaces. (*Leaching* refers to the effect of water in dissolving materials and transporting them downward—either from plant surfaces to the soil or from upper soil levels to lower.) Table 5·1 gives data on nutrient leaching for a British oak forest. The second row of numbers gives the percentage of the total amount of a nutrient that reaches the soil from above, that does so by being leached from plant surfaces and carried down in rainwater. For two of the nutrients—potassium and sodium— a larger fraction of the element reaches the soil by washing from leaf and bark surfaces than by fall of dead leaves. Nitrogen shows a negative leaching effect, implying that it is being extracted from the water flowing across plant surfaces. This extraction may be primarily uptake by organisms (lichens, algae, and bacteria) on bark and leaf surfaces. As in aquatic communities also, the surfaces of organisms often support films or crusts of other organisms active in nutrient uptake. The water that reaches the forest floor contains also a quite significant amount of organic carbon, as indicated in the last column of the table. The greater part of this carbon was in a triple sugar, melezitose, from the secretions of aphids, a smaller part in the form of phenolic compounds.

A much larger amount of organic carbon falls on the forest floor as leaf and branch litter. The litter is attacked by soil animals, bacteria, and fungi, and by their variously combined efforts is broken down and degraded to release nutrients back into the soil. The rate of decomposition of the litter and the rates of release of the different nutrients varies widely, however. Some forms of litter (wood, conifer needles, sclerophyll leaves) are more resistant to decomposition than others (broadleaf deciduous and tropical rainforest leaves). There is in addition a broad correlation of decay rate with temperature: decay rates are slow in cold climates and faster in hot climates.

TABLE 5·1

Movement of Nutrients into the Soil in an English Oak Woodland. (Carlisle et al., *Jour. Ecol.*, 54:87, 1966; see also 55:615, 1967). Values in the first three rows are percentages of the total nutrient weights in the fourth row.

	Nitro-gen	Phos-phorus	Potas-sium	Cal-cium	Magne-sium	So-dium	Car-bon
Percentage in the precipitation above the canopy	19.1	12.3	7.7	17.8	35.0	61.8	2.4
Added to the precipitation by washing from plant surfaces	−1.4	25.1	65.1	24.1	35.8	35.3	8.0
In litter fall of dead leaves and branches	82.3	62.6	27.2	58.1	29.3	2.9	89.6
Total weight of element added to the soil, kg/ha/yr	49.9	3.5	38.6	41.0	13.2	57.2	2186.

(Although different organic remains in the litter of a given community decompose at different rates, it is possible to express the overall rate of decomposition in the forms

$$\frac{dM}{dt} = L - kM \qquad M_t = M_o\, e^{-kt}$$

L is the rate of litter fall in mass per unit area per unit time and M is the total mass of litter present per unit area. For the decay process, M_o is an initial mass of litter that is reduced to mass M_t by decomposition through time t; k is an instantaneous decay rate analogous to the λ of radioactive decay, and e is the base of natural logarithms. If the litter mass is in steady state, $dM/dt = 0$, and $L = kM$. If $M_t = 0.5\, M_o$, then t becomes a half life or half time—the time required for one half of the organic matter present in the litter and soil at a given time to decompose to inorganic form.) Half times for decomposition of organic matter of litter are of the order of more than ten years in northern coniferous forests, one to a few years in temperate deciduous and southern pine forests, fractions of years in tropical rain forests.

In humid tropical areas decomposition is rapid, and strong leaching of nutrients downward leaves oxides of iron and aluminum behind to make up a large part of the material of red tropical forest soils (laterites). Although tropical soils vary widely, many such soils are of low organic content, great depth, tight nutrient circulation, and rapid loss of fertility when cleared for cultivation. In northern forest or taiga areas decomposition is slow, but the organic acids that are formed leach iron, aluminum, and other nutrients downward, leaving a layer of light-colored sand beneath the litter. Nutrients and clay are deposited in a layer beneath this, but such taiga soils (podzols) are of low pH (high acidity), and generally low fertility under cultivation. Apart from some forms of intensive cultivation, high rainfall in tropical and far-northern climates may yield small profit in agriculture. The best soils for human purposes are those of climates of intermediate temperatures, and especially some of those of the intermediate moisture conditions that support grasslands.

Organic Circulation

The sugar from aphids washed downward from foliage to soil in the oak forest becomes food for some soil microorganisms. Actually, a wide variety of organic materials are excreted or leached from the surfaces of higher plants, both into rainwater above ground and from roots into soil water below ground. Plankton algae also lose into the water substantial fractions of the organic material they synthesize. Because of this leakage from plant cells, together with animal excretion and the enzymatic effects of bacteria living on the surface of particles of dead organic matter, the water of the oceans and lakes generally contains much more organic material in solution than in living organisms and dead particles. Many aquatic plants and animals are able to absorb some of this dissolved material to supplement their nutrition by photosynthesis or ingestion.

Uptake of foods, and also of vitamins, directly from the water is especially important to many of the unicellular organisms. These unicellular organisms are both actively losing organic matter to the water and actively absorbing organic matter—primarily different substances. Even among the forms possessing chloroplasts many are dependent on external, dissolved organic matter; they live by mixtures of autotrophic and heterotrophic nutrition, mixtures that differ from species to species in the proportion of the heterotrophic needs and the identity of the organic compounds that are required from the water. There is thus active circulation of organic matter in the plankton that does not move through the classical food chains. It is also true that population dynamics of plankton are affected by the organic materials in the water and that different species occupy, by virtue of different substances released and required, different positions in the organic circulation of the ecosystem.

Along with nutrient ions, foods, and vitamins the plankton cells are releasing wastes into the water. The organic wastes of one species may well be food for another. Some of the substances released may also be effective toxins. The common green alga *Chlorella* releases a compound, chlorellin, that has an inhibiting effect on the growth of other algal species, on the rate of grazing by plankton animals, and (if concentrations are high) on the growth of *Chlorella* itself. Chlorellin is one of very many compounds released into environment by organisms that exert an inhibiting or repellent effect on other organisms. The antibiotics released by certain bacteria and fungi are the most widely known of such compounds because of their great medical value to man. Their value to man lies in their inhibition of bacterial growth; their value to the fungi that secrete them doubtless lies in the same direction. They are agents of chemical warfare between species; their release into an environment can, in some circumstances, give the fungus an advantage by killing or inhibiting the growth of other organisms that might otherwise compete with the fungus for food. Certain lichens of rock surfaces in the Arctic produce bare zones around them by release of chemicals which suppress other lichens (Figure 5·4A).

Many fungi and mycelial bacteria of the forest floor produce chemical agents that affect other species. So, however, do higher plants. The monarch butterfly is celebrated as a protected species—as unpalatable to taste as it is striking in color—which is mimicked by another butterfly, the viceroy. The monarch feeds as a caterpillar on plants that are also chemically protected, those of the milkweed family. The milkweed plants are unpalatable to most insects because of repellent chemicals concentrated in their tissues, but the monarch and its relatives, and some other insects, have evolved the ability to tolerate these chemicals and feed on milkweed tissues. The monarch butterfly has in a further evolutionary step turned this tolerance to advantage: it utilizes, through its own metabolism, the repellent substances of the milkweed plant to make itself repellent to predators. It is the monarch's success in the biochemical interplay among species that makes it a protected model, which it has been to the evolutionary advantage of the viceroy to mimic.

Analyses of the tissues of higher plants have revealed the existence of a wide range of secondary plant substances—organic compounds that are abundant in certain plants, but are widely variable in concentration and occurrence among different kinds of plants, and that have no known role in essential metabolic processes. Among these substances are several large groups—phenolic substances including tannins, terpenoids including many of the aromatic substances of plants and resins, alkaloids and organic cyanides—and a number of other, less widely distributed groups. It is likely that these substances form a spectrum from wastes of the plant's metabolism through wastes that are concentrated in plant tissues because of the advantage they give in repelling the plant's enemies, to compounds secreted only for their protective value. Secondary plant substances (but not necessarily the same compounds) may offer protection against both consuming animals and parasitic bacteria and fungi. Many of these substances are potentially toxic to the plant itself. Concentrations that give effective protection are possible, however, when the substances are isolated or stored in chemically inactive states in the plant (as in the combination of a toxic alkaloid with a sugar) but become actively toxic when released from the plant or eaten by an animal.

Like antibiotics, and like the many repellent compounds of animals, secondary plant substances are apparently armaments in the widespread biochemical combat in natural communities. The evolutionary interplay of plants and insect consumers (or other enemies) probably proceeds as follows:

1. A plant species evolves a device for chemical protection against animals; thus protected, the plants increase in abundance and differentiate into a group of species, or ultimately a family.

2. Certain insect species evolve a tolerance of the chemical protection; these insect species in turn may increase and diversify as consumers of the plants in relative freedom from competition.

3. Consumption by the insects brings selection for intensification of the chemical protection in the plant, thus bringing also intensified selection for tolerance in the animals. A balanced biochemical accommodation of plant and animal to each other is likely to evolve.

4. The insect may, meanwhile, evolve to turn the plant's protective chemistry to its own advantage—its own protection or as a behavioral cue by which females may locate and identify plants on which to lay eggs.

   Some plants, however, have come upon a particularly successful tactic in this combat—evolution by the plant of secretion of the hormones of insect moulting and metamorphosis, that prevent completion of life cycles by insects feeding on the plant. Some plants are in consequence nearly (but not necessarily completely) immune to insect consumption.

The concentration of secondary plant substances in plant tissues, whether wastes or repellents or both, is often such that substantial quantities are leaked into the environment. Here they may have significant effects on other vascular plants, on soil animals, bacteria and fungi, and even on the plant population from which they are released. Concentration in the soil of secondary plant substances from a dominant plant may exclude many other plant species from the community. In southern California shrubs of the soft chaparral, a community of low, aromatic shrubs, are able to spread into some areas of grassland. During dry periods on clay soils, plants of the grassland are largely

Figure 5·4. Chemical antagonism between organisms. A: Antibiotic effects between lichens. The lichen in the center (*Rhizocarpon* cf. *rittokense*) has prevented by
release of a chemical agent the growth of other lichen species in the bare belt surrounding it, in which the light-colored rock (gneiss) can be seen. Because the chemicals
are carried in moving water, the belt is wider on the lower edge of the lichen patch;
the patch is 13 cm in diameter, the inhibition zone up to 6 cm wide. [Photo taken
at Torssukatak Fiord, West Greenland; courtesy of and copyright by R. E. Beschel.]
B: Allelopathic effects between vascular plants. Volatile terpenes released by the
shrubs on the left (*Salvia leucophylla,* of the soft chaparral) are adsorbed on the
particles of a clay soil and inhibit germination and growth of plants of the annual
grassland. During a dry period when the effect was most intense, the belt of bare
ground surrounding the shrubs was 2 m wide, and partial inhibition of the grassland
species extended about 6 m from the shrubs. [Photo taken near Santa Barbara, California; courtesy of and copyright by C. H. Muller; see also Muller, 1966.]

116

excluded from the shrub patches and from a fringe a meter or more in width around the shrub patches (Figure 5·4B). The exclusion is by some of the same substances that render the shrub community aromatic—terpenes, notably cineole and camphor. These volatile chemicals are released into the atmosphere by the shrubs and adsorbed onto soil particles during the dry season, and in the rainy season they inhibit the germination and growth of annual plants. Such effects of chemicals derived from a higher plant in inhibiting the growth of other higher plants are termed *allelopathic*. Substances of established or suspected allelopathic effect are known in a very wide range of terrestrial communities—desert and grassland, shrubland and forest—and in all the major groups of secondary plant substances. Water-soluble substances of the phenolic grouping appear to be more important in more humid climates, volatile substances of the terpenoid grouping in some more arid climates. The routes by which these allelopathic compounds affect other plants are varied—adsorption of volatile materials in the soil, leaching of soluble materials from leaves down to the soil, release from decaying leaves and litter, and release from living roots or from dead roots by decomposition by bacteria and fungi.

Shrubs of the soft chaparral dominate the community by chemical influences, as well as by root competition and microclimatic effects. Allelopathic effects appear to be significant in many stable communities of strong single-species dominance. In these communities the chemistry of the soil may be much affected by the secondary substance chemistry of the dominant plant species, and only those other species that are tolerant of this chemistry can maintain populations in the community. Forests of strong dominance by a single tree species have often a meager undergrowth of low species-diversity, in contrast with the richer undergrowth of many forests of mixed dominance.

In unstable communities of strong single-species dominance allelopathic substances can also become autopathic or autotoxic, inhibiting the growth of the dominant species itself. Older patches of the soft chaparral shrubs show reduced vigor in consequence of the accumulation of their own secondary substances. Certain plants of successions (*Hieracium* and *Erigeron* species) produce chemical effects in the soil that destroy their own populations in one or a few years, when they are replaced by other species more tolerant of these chemical effects. Autotoxic effects or self-inhibiting effects are known for *Chlorella* and other algae. Autotoxicity would not seem a profitable direction of evolution. Presumably, for some species of unstable communities, there has been greater selective advantage in the evolution of high concentrations of the secondary substances as repellents, than selective disadvantage from the effects of these substances on the short-lived populations of the species itself.

The environments of communities, the soil and water, contain diverse organic compounds of varied significance to populations in ways other than for food energy; these include vitamins and enzymes, wastes and decomposition products, antibiotics and allelopathics, repellents and attractants, and hormones and message compounds (pheromones) between individuals of a species. Substances produced by one species that are significant to another species for stimulation or inhibition of growth or antagonistic effect or behavioral influence, and not for food value, may be collectively termed *allelochemic* materials. They are part of the chemical interplay by which organisms of an ecosystem are related. The function of ecosystems involves a triple traffic of substances of three broad groupings—inorganic nutrients, foods, and allelochemics—moving through varied routes in a chemical arabesque. The combined production, circulation, and utilization and effects of these substances represents a community-level metabolism, the complexity of which approaches that of the metabolism of organisms.

A Watershed

The chemical linkages of organisms and environments need, however, to be followed into a broader context. A plankton community is part of a water body; a forest is part of a landscape. We may profitably expand our interest from a forest stand to a mountain drainage basin or watershed as a landscape unit, and treat this as a larger ecosystem.

Small forested watersheds at Hubbard Brook, New Hampshire, have been studied in this way. The water leaving a watershed flows through a weir, a gauging device by which the volume of water flowing out of the watershed at different times can be measured. Chemical analysis of the water at different seasons makes possible calculation of the amounts of nutrient elements leaving the watershed in a year (output, Table 5·2). A relatively small part of the output is in the form of particulate matter—soil and rock particles, fragments of dead leaves, and so on—carried in the water. Because the forest is in a condition approaching climax, the output of nutrients from the ecosystem should be balanced by input.

Rainfall also has been measured, and rainwater chemistry analyzed, around the year. Input in rainfall of several elements is indicated in Table 5·2. The amounts for the first four elements are not enough to balance the output, and there must be an additional source of nutrients for the ecosystem. This source is the soil-forming process, which gradually weathers and decomposes the parent rock (granite and glacial till) underlying the soils of the watershed and releases soluble inorganic nutrients into the soil. The weathering process is difficult to measure directly, but in the steady-state system the amounts released should

TABLE 5·2
Nutrient Budgets for Five Elements in Forested Watersheds in the White Mountains, New Hampshire. Values are kg/ha/yr ($= g/m^2/yr$ times 10). (Cations are four-year averages, Johnson et al., *Geochim. Cosmochim. Acta*, 32:531, 1968; nitrogens of ammonia and nitrates are two-year averages, Bormann et al., *Science*, 159:882, 1968.)

	Precipitation input	Streamflow output	Difference
Calcium	2.6	10.6	+8.0
Sodium	1.5	6.1	+4.6
Magnesium	0.7	2.5	+1.8
Potassium	1.4	1.5	+0.1
NH_4—Nitrogen	2.1	0.6	−1.5
NO_3—Nitrogen	3.6	1.2	−2.4

approximately equal the "difference" values in Table 5·2. Calculations based on sodium and calcium indicate that the parent rock is weathered at a rate of 800 kg/ha/yr. This rate is approximately equivalent to a lowering of the rock surface (by complete weathering) to a depth of 50 cm in the 14,000 years since glaciation, hence about 0.04 mm/yr. Nutrient function of the watershed thus involves a balancing of nutrient input by precipitation and weathering with output in the stream, for the watershed as a whole. This balancing is in addition to the balancing of uptake by plants and return to the soil within the forest communities.

The pattern of nutrient function is quite different for nitrogen (in the forms of ammonia and nitrates in Table 5·2). Nitrogen in forms available to plants is being added to the forest ecosystem by nitrification—fixing of atmospheric nitrogen by bacteria—and is also lost from the forest by denitrification. There is active cycling of nitrogen between the atmosphere and the forest ecosystem, with nitrogen entering the ecosystem by way of both precipitation and nitrification, and returning from forest to atmosphere by way of denitrification. The output of nitrogen (ammonia, nitrates, and organic compounds) in the stream water is relatively small. The forest effectively holds against loss by leaching the nitrogen in forms available to forest organisms. The extent to which the community holds its nutrients was shown in one of the Hubbard Brook watersheds by cutting all trees and killing all undergrowth plants, leaving the dead remains of the trees and other plants on the ground. Following the cutting nitrate-nitrogen drained from the watershed in the stream at a rate of 53.6 kg/ha/yr, compared with the mean output of 1.2 kg/ha/yr indicated in Table 5·2 for an uncut, control watershed. Losses of other nutrients in the stream also rose abruptly after the forest was cut.

The undisturbed forest in contrast has a self-regulating, self-protective function. The forest cover protects the soils supporting the forest against erosion. Much of the rainwater penetrates into the soil and leaves it in a slow and continuing manner by uptake and transpiration by plants, and subsurface flow within the soil downhill and into the stream. The forest holds its nutrients in the soil and in plant tissues, and thus limits to varying degrees the loss from these stocks of nutrients by leaching and erosion. The forest maintains an organic structure amounting at Hubbard Brook to probably 20 to 30 kg/m² of dry biomass. A trivial fraction of this biomass (about 1.3 kg/m², or 0.005% per year) leaves the watershed in the stream as particulate organic matter and represents net ecosystem production by the forest which may be available as food for stream organisms outside the watershed. The stream water is relatively constant in its concentrations of dissolved nutrient elements despite the changes in volume of stream water after storms and in different seasons. The water, most of which reaches the stream by subsurface movement in the soil, is largely stabilized in its chemical composition by its interaction with the soil it flows through. When the forest is cut or burned the stabilizing functions of the ecosystem are destroyed. The soil on these mountain slopes may then be subject to rapid erosion. The greater part of the water then moves on the soil surface, rather than leaving the forest by transpiration and subsurface flow; and after a storm the rapid loss of water from the ecosystem is the means of rapid removal of nutrients, soil, and organic material.

The rate of nutrient output from a watershed for different elements is affected by the manner in which these elements are taken up and held in the community and soil—the degree to which a given element is bound into organic matter and held in tight circulation. No matter how tight the circulation, however, some loss of nutrients in water moving under and over the soil surface into the stream is inevitable. The level of production of the forest must be to some degree affected, and in the long term limited, by the rate of nutrient input. This observation raises points of interest: (1) Life on land is to a degree dependent on the weathering process to replace nutrients that must be lost from the soil by transport in moving water. (2) Rainwater is "pure," but not pure like distilled water. Life on land is also to a degree dependent on the inorganic nutrients in precipitation, which become part of the nutrient function of natural and agricultural communities.

Biogeochemical Circulation

The question of where the nutrients in precipitation come from is an important one. They come, in large part, from the sea. Over the 70 per cent of the earth's surface that is ocean, winds and wave-spray mix droplets of sea water into the lower atmosphere; the droplets evaporate to leave particles of salts in the air, and turbulence and convection mix these upward in the atmosphere. The particles may later, over the land, serve as the condensation centers for snow, or may be dissolved into raindrops, or may settle; in any case they become part of the nutrient content of precipitation.

Thus it is likely that a sodium ion that reaches a wheatfield in Kansas in the summer has arrived in air from over the Gulf of Mexico; whereas sodium washed from the field into a stream is on its way back to the Gulf of Mexico. It is possible for an ion to do a year's tour of duty in the nutrient circulation of a wheatfield, between years in which it participates in the water chemistry and nutrient function of the marine plankton ecosystem. The reader will recognize that the land and the sea are coupled in nutrient circulation, that the expanding context in which nutrient circulation should be studied leads ultimately to the world ecosystem. The study of world-wide chemical circulation, concentration, deposit, and release is the subject of *biogeochemistry*.

The proportions of elements in rainwater, Table 5·1, do not simply correspond to their proportions in sea water. Calcium and nitrogen, for example, are several times as abundant (considered not in absolute amounts but by ratios to sodium) in rainwater as in sea water. Our statement of the marine origin of the nutrients in precipitation must be modified for these and other elements. The proportion of calcium in precipitation increases from the coast inland in some areas. Some of the calcium in the precipitation comes from the ocean, but much comes from dust from land surfaces, mixed upward into the atmosphere in one place and brought down again (either as particles or in solution) in another area. A primary source of the calcium is the dust from soils in areas of limestone rocks, for limestone is predominantly $CaCO_3$. It is not the case that this calcium is simply terrestrial in origin, however, for limestone is a rock deposited on the ocean bottom and brought to the surface on land millions of years later by geological processes. There are thus two major routes by which calcium circulates from sea to land—a shorter term route by sea-spray into the atmosphere, and a larger and longer term route of deposit, formation of rock, elevation

of rock, exposure, weathering, and dust. Major features of the biogeochemical cycle for calcium are illustrated in Figure 5·5.

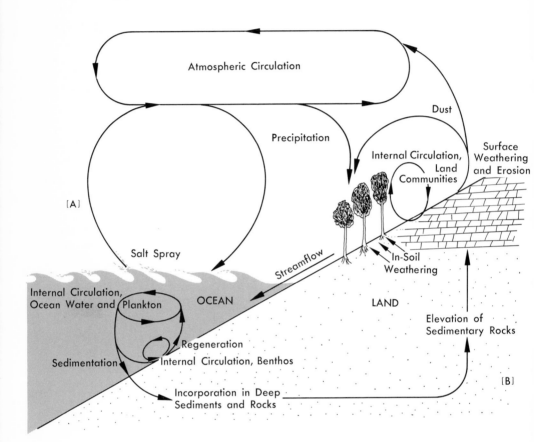

**Figure 5·5. Major features of biogeochemical cycles for calcium and other
elements.** Circulations within ecosystems, on land and in the sea, are linked into the
global circulation through cycles. **A:** Shorter term cycles from the ocean surface into
the atmosphere by salt spray, into terrestrial ecosystems by precipitation, and back
to the ocean in stream water. **B:** Longer term cycles from ocean waters into deep
sediments and rocks, to exposure on land surfaces after elevation of these rocks, and
back to the ocean by varied routes involving in-soil weatherng, dust, streamflow, or
atmospheric circulation and precipitation.

As in the aquarium study, some features of biogeochemical cycles
can be represented in patterns of pool magnitudes and transfer rates.
Figure 5·6 is an example of a biogeochemical cycle thus treated. Pool
magnitudes are in this case expressed as average amounts per unit of
the earth's surface, transfer rates in average quantities transferred per
unit of the earth's surface (in contrast with the rates as decimal frac-

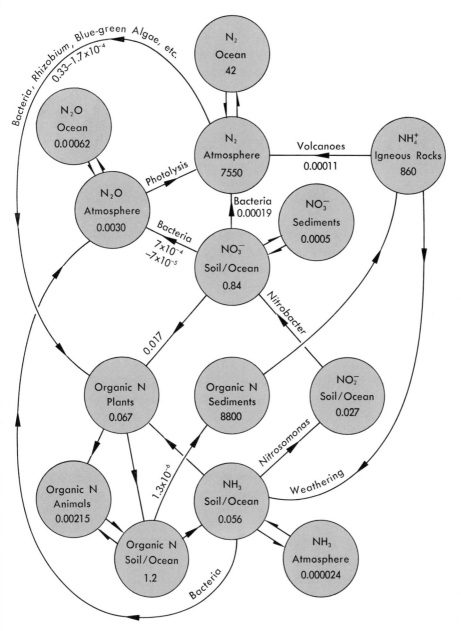

Figure 5·6. The biogeochemical cycle for nitrogen. Numbers in circles are amounts of nitrogen in pools, in kilograms per square meter of the earth's surface; numbers on arrows are transfer rates in kilograms of nitrogen per square meter per year. [Bowen, 1966.]

tions, in Figure 5·2). In biogeochemical treatment the degree to which the substance in a pool is in flux is often expressed as *residence time*. (Loss from the pool may be expressed as output rate (R_o) in mass per unit time, t

$$R_o = M(1 - e^{-kt})$$

If the pool is in steady state, the input rate and the output rate $(R_o = kM)$ are equal. M is the total mass of the substance in the pool and k is an instantaneous rate constant. The treatment is in parallel with that for turnover of soil organic matter above, and radioisotopes in organisms, below. If r is the sum of the decimal fraction transfer rates for output from the pool, t_r is residence time, and $t_{.5}$ is turnover half time, then

$$t_r = M/R_o = 1/k = 1.44t_{.5} = -1/ln(1-r)$$

relating the various rate expressions to one another.) Residence time or turnover time is the magnitude of the pool divided by the amount leaving per unit time. Residence times for nitrogen are of the order of 3×10^8 years for atmospheric N_2, 2,500 years for nitrogen in the sea (treating nitrogen of nitrates and organic compounds as a single pool), generally less than a year for nitrates and nitrites in the soil.

The nitrogen cycle has been extensively studied because of the great importance of nitrogen as a nutrient element. Nitrogen is abundantly present in the environment, forming about four fifths of the atmosphere. This abundance of nitrogen is not simply available to higher organisms: apparently no higher land plant is able by itself to take in and utilize atmospheric nitrogen in its metabolism. A scattering of lower organisms, primarily procaryotic ones, are able to do so. Some blue-green algae fix significant amounts of nitrogen in the oceans, lakes, and the soil. Symbiotic bacteria in root nodules of legumes, plants of the pea family (and also species of alder, buckbrush, and a number of other genera that are not legumes) fix atmospheric nitrogen. The relation is mutualistic, for the bacteria use energy from the vascular plant to fix nitrogen, that is made available to the host plant and other plants of the community.

A pair of widespread genera of bacteria of the oceans and soil, *Nitrosomonas* and *Nitrobacter,* convert ammonia into nitrite, and nitrite into nitrate. These bacteria primarily use the energy of dead organic matter to convert ammonia from dead organic matter (protein residues, and so on) into nitrates available to higher plants. Their role is thus not primarily fixation of atmospheric nitrogen but participation in the circulation of nitrogen within ecosystems. Other, denitrifying bacteria break down nitrates and release molecular nitrogen back to the atmosphere. Other routes of nitrogen fixation exist, including

other bacteria, certain fungi, and the action of lightning in the atmosphere (from which some part of the nitrogen in the precipitation of
Table 5·1 is derived).

Some points of interest on the nitrogen cycle and biogeochemistry
are

1. The existence of an invisible dependence of the higher organisms
    upon a few of the lower. The higher, eucaryotic organisms are
    largely dependent on certain bacteria and blue-green algae for
    nitrogen fixation and nitrogen circulation, without which the func-
    tion of natural communities would slow down to a much lower
    level. It is estimated that about 90 per cent of fixed nitrogen is fixed
    by organisms, about 10 per cent by lightning, and that man's total
    application of agricultural fertilizer is about 10 per cent of the
    amount of nitrogen fixed by microorganisms.

2. The existence of steady states on different levels of nitrogen circu-
    lation, as of other biogeochemical circulations. In a steady-state
    forest the rate of nitrogen input by precipitation and organic nitri-
    fication will balance output by denitrification and groundwater
    and stream loss. Rate of input to the ocean by streamflow, precipi-
    tation, and nitrification together should equal loss by denitrification
    and deposit in bottom sediments. In the biosphere at large, the loss
    by sedimentation and denitrification should equal the gain by
    nitrification, weathering, volcanic release of ammonia, and light-
    ning fixation. It is not known what change in this steady-state
    system of interlinked steady-state systems may be occurring. Man,
    however, is increasing fertilization of agricultural fields (and there-
    fore of the water bodies into which streams from these fields flow).

3. The significance of these cycles for the dissolved substances in the
    sea, as well as those of soil waters and streams. It is familiar that
    life evolved through most of its history in the sea, and that land and
    fresh-water organisms bear the imprint of sea-water chemistry in
    their chemistry of inorganic ions. The blood of man resembles a
    dilute form of the sea water to which his earlier chordate ancestors
    were adapted. It may be less evident that the chemistry of the sea
    is profoundly influenced by organisms. Concentration of an ele-
    ment in sea water is by no means determined simply by its solu-
    bility and abundance in weathering products of rocks and in stream
    water. Concentrations are determined by the need of organisms
    for substances and the consequent rate of removal and deposit in
    sediments, in relation to the input by streams and solubility. Some
    elements are abundant in sea water because they are in small de-
    mand by organisms relative to their high solubility and input rates;
    these have long residence times and include sodium (2.6×10^8

yrs.), magnesium (4.5×10^7 yrs.), potassium (11×10^6 yrs.), calcium (8×10^6 yrs.), chlorine, and sulphur. Other elements exist in the ocean in much lower concentrations despite high input rates, because of the demand for these substances by organisms and consequent loss to the bottom sediments; these include silicon (8×10^3 yrs.), nitrogen (2.5×10^3 yrs.), manganese (1.4×10^3 yrs.), and phosphorus. Like soil chemistry, sea water chemistry is so edited and amended by organisms as to obscure the composition of the original text—the geological input by weathering.

4. The complexity of the biogeochemical circulation, and the biogeochemical linkages of land, sea, atmosphere, soil, and organisms. Each element or substance has its own pattern of biogeochemical circulation, differing at least in quantitative details from those of all other elements. All together these cycles, and the moving air and water which are an important part of their mechanism, imply that the local ecosystems of the world are woven into a world-ecosystem, the biosphere (or, considering that the biosphere is its living part only, the ecosphere). Man is part of the world ecosystem, and its environment is man's environment.

Radioisotope Contamination

Such is the background from which problems of environmental pollution are to be understood. Experiences with radioisotopes have provided valuable instruction in the meaning of pollution processes.

During the Second World War water of the Columbia River was used to cool plutonium-producing reactors at the Hanford Works in eastern Washington. The intense neutron flux in the reactors made certain elements in the water radioactive. Retention of the water in basins for a period during which much of its radioactivity decayed, dilution of the water in the large volume of the river, and careful monitoring of the radioactivity of river water and organisms were means of ensuring that no hazard to human health developed. The levels of radiophosphorus and other isotopes in the Columbia River organisms were not hazardous, but they were sufficient to emphasize the necessity of control measures to prevent hazard. Decreasing levels of radioactivity in water and organisms could be traced down the Columbia River and into the Pacific Ocean.

Other radioactive materials escaped from the smokestacks of Hanford and other atomic plants. Contamination by this means of the atmosphere and vegetation has required the study of concentration of radioiodine and other isotopes in terrestrial vertebrate animals. Tests of atomic weapons up until the test limitation treaty of 1963 released increasing amounts of radioactive materials into the atmosphere.

These materials were carried into the upper atmosphere and circulated around the earth, and settled to produce measurable increases in radioactivity in precipitation over the whole of the earth's surface. One weapon test showered radioactive dust on a Japanese fishing ship and spread unexpected amounts of radioactivity to Pacific islands, the ocean waters, and tuna and other fish. In general the amount of fallout from weapon tests has not been sufficient to constitute a short-term physiological hazard to man, or so far as is known to other organisms, outside the restricted areas in which the tests were carried out.

Exposure of organisms to radioactive materials implies exposure of their protoplasm (especially, the nuclei of their cells) to adverse effects of ionizing irradiation. Radioactive materials in the environment are consequently toxic pollutants. Ionizing radiation produces interrelated effects on three time scales: (1) intense, and usually acute or short-term, exposure producing acute radiation sickness, (2) lower-level, and often chronic, exposures producing in the individuals exposed delayed consequences, which may include cancer and relatively subtle effects in accelerated aging, and (3) effects, which can occur at low levels of exposure, on the genetic material of the reproductive cells, effects that are expressed as unfavorable mutations in descendants of the organism exposed. All three effects may occur primarily from damaging hits by ionizing radiation on or near the genetic material in nuclei—the chromosomes. The sensitivity of organisms to radiation effects is in consequence strongly affected by the mean volume of chromosomes. Sensitivity varies widely among kinds of organisms: man and other vertebrates are sensitive, arthropods and many plants are less sensitive, microorganisms relatively insensitive.

Low levels of natural or background radioactivity in consequence of naturally radioactive elements and cosmic rays exist throughout the world. These low levels of natural ionizing radiation are responsible for part of the natural mutation rate of organisms, although hits by ionizing radiation in general account for a minority of mutations. An organism has a complement of genes that has resulted from long-term selection. The genes selected for are both individually favorable and favorable in their interrelations in the whole genetic system of the organism and species. The great majority of mutations are necessarily deleterious, even if some few mutations are advantageous and their selection is the basis of evolution. Increasing the level of environmental radiation has the inescapable consequence of increasing the numbers of unfavorable mutant genes, genes whose effects on human beings range from the mildly disadvantageous to the tragic. It is this less obvious genetic effect of radiation, which has no threshold and occurs at levels far below those of direct, physiological radiation damage, that has been of most concern. The treaty limiting aboveground testing of atomic weapons by the major atomic powers (though by no means a complete and permanent solution to the problems of radiation release into the environment) is one of civilized man's greatest achievements in limiting the destructive implications of technology.

The broadcasting of radioisotopes into the air, water, and soil has brought concern both with isotopes of elements of known biological significance (tritium or hydrogen-3, carbon-14, phosphorus-32, sulphur-35, potassium-40, calcium-45, manganese-54, iron-59, iodine-131, and so on) and with those of a number of elements exotic to the chemistry of life (rubidium-86, strontium-90 and yttrium-90, zirconium-95 cesium-134, cerium-144, ruthenium-106, plutonium-239). Some of these have been of special concern as pollutants. Radioiodine is of concern to man because of its concentration along food chains from low levels in the environment to relatively high levels in the thyroid gland. Radiostrontium is a pollutant of major importance because of its similarity in chemical behavior to calcium. Strontium-90 is concentrated from low levels in the environment to higher levels in human bones; the concentration ratios are highest in children who are adding calcium to bone more rapidly than adults and who receive strontium in milk as well as in other foods. Cesium-137 is taken up by plants along with potassium. One of the least expected hazards to human beings involved food-chain concentration of cesium from atomic particles to soil and lichens in the arctic tundra to reindeer feeding on these lichens to Eskimos eating the reindeer.

(If the radioisotope and its nonradioactive relative are at stable levels in an aquatic environment, and certain other simplifying assumptions are accepted, then environmental radioactivity for the isotope may be expressed as

$$D_e = C_e I_e A_i$$

(D_e, the activity density of the water, its radioactivity measured in curies per gram of water) $= (C_e$, concentration of the nonradioactive isotope or element per gram of water) $\times (I_e$, isotopic dilution or ratio by numbers of atoms of the radioisotope to the nonradioactive equivalent) $\times (A_i$, the specific activity in curies per gram of the isotope). The concentration ratio of the nonradioactive element is $R = C_o/C_e$, C_o being the concentration of the element in grams per gram of the organism (by dry weight, or in some treatments by live weight). The corresponding concentration ratio for the radioisotope is R', and D_o is the equilibrium activity density for the organism

$$D_o = R'D_e = C_o I_e A_i e^{-\lambda t}$$

(The concentration ratios for the stable, naturally occurring isotope or element (R) and for the radioactive isotope (R') are not identical because of the effect of radioactive decay on the latter. There may, furthermore, be measurable difference in the chemical behavior of the radioisotope and the nonradioactive equivalent in uptake and metabolism, but the equation has not been complicated to allow for this difference. The constant of radioactive decay for the isotope is λ; t is the time for the isotope in biological transfer and metabolism and includes (a) mean residence time for an atom of the isotope in the pool of atoms of that isotope within the organism, and (b) food-chain time, time spent by the isotope moving along a food chain from environment to food source if the isotope is taken up in food rather than directly from environment. The approach of the organism's radioactivity to equilibrium after its introduction to a polluted environment (or after the beginning of a stable level of pollution of its environment) is

$$D_t = D_o(1 - e^{-(k+\lambda)t})$$

In this D_t is the activity density of the organism at time t; and k is treated as a constant, analogous to λ, for rate of loss by turnover and excretion of atoms from the pool of the element in the tissues of the organism and is related to time (a) above.)

Concentration of a radioisotope in an organism (activity density, D_o, in curies per gram) is necessarily greater with higher isotopic dilution ratio (I_e). The ratio is increased by either increased abundance of the pollutant isotope, or scarcity of its nonradioactive relative, or by both. Activity density must also increase with a high concentration ratio. As observed, activity concentration ratios of one and two million times for radiophosphorus can result from the high elemental concentration ratio (R) when nonradioactive phosphate is scarce in the water. Ratios for many other elements are measured in thousands or tens of thousands. High decay constant (λ) values express rapid loss of radioactivity by the radioisotope and imply that the concentration ratio for this isotope (R') will be markedly lower than that for the element (R). A number of radioisotopes of short half lives that are abundant products of reactors and atomic weapons are of minor concern in the environment under most circumstances. Concentration of these isotopes will be lower in animals if the time (t) includes food-chain time (but some of these isotopes are directly absorbed from fresh water by animals). In some cases, however, concentration of the inactive relative of the radioisotope (C_o) increases up a food chain from plants to animals, and from herbivorous animals to carnivorous ones. In this case concentration ratios for the isotope and radioactivity of tissues may increase up a food chain. Such may be the case despite the fact that the approach to equilibrium, as expressed in the last equation above, is slower in larger organisms.

In general, sensitivity to radioactivity also increases up the food chain. It will be noted that for higher animals the crucial concentration ratios are those that apply not to the whole organism, but to particular tissues in which a given isotope is concentrated—e.g., the thyroid gland for iodine, bone for strontium. There is a tendency, despite wide differences in species on a given trophic level, for potential effects of radiopollution to hit hardest those organisms that are highest in food-chain level and in evolutionary level.

Man is low in neither sense, and would suffer the consequences of extensive release of radioactive materials accordingly. Some featured points that have emerged from experience with radioisotope contamination to date (and that are closely related to observations on tracers in microcosms) are

1. The effectiveness of world-wide transport in wind and water, and the unity of the biosphere in consequence of this transport.
2. The effectiveness of organisms and food chains in concentration processes, and the manner in which biosphere transfer and concentration by organisms collaborate to produce those hazards that develop.
3. The variety and complexity of transfer and concentration routes and patterns, the variation in detail despite similarity in principle that affects different isotopes and elements.
4. The partial unpredictableness of the patterns and hazards. Though relevant principles of biogeochemical circulation and ecosystem function are understood, detailed effects are not simply predictable and hazards may be discovered only when already well advanced. Unwelcome surprises are normal among pollution effects.

Pesticides

Since the Second World War there has also been a rapid increase in release into the environment of poisons that kill organisms unwelcome to man. Among these are poisons of most varied character aimed at insects and mites, nematodes and fungi, fish, rodents and mammalian predators, and algae and higher plants. The most massive uses of poisons are against man's principal rivals for consumption of agricultural crops—insect pests. In the diversity of chemical agents used against insects two families of compounds are of most concern.

The organophosphate compounds include parathion, malathion, chlorthion, phosdrin, and others. These poisons are inhibitors of the enzyme cholinesterase, important in the transmission of nerve impulses; they block in particular the normal function of synapses. These substances are among the most intensively effective poisons known; their use in most cases requires stringent controls to avoid human exposure. Sensitivity to their effects on nervous function is shared by arthropod targets and vertebrates, including man; parathion in particular has gained from cases of poisoning a reputation for lethality to man. Aquatic organisms seem in general less affected than terrestrial ones. The organophosphates are relatively unstable both in environments and in tissues; they are consequently little subject to the processes of dispersion and accumulation observed in the chlorinated hydrocarbons. They can produce extensive mortality of organisms other than the target pests in areas where they are applied, and they can disturb the interactions on which biological control (by predators and parasites of the pest species) may have been based. They do not in general, however, spread widely through environments or accumulate in environments or in tissues.

The organophosphate poisons are of much less serious concern in pollution effects than the chlorinated hydrocarbons (DDT, chlordane, dieldrin, endrin, aldrin, heptachlor, toxaphene, lindane, and so on). These poisons combine intense toxicity to a wide range of kinds of organisms with relative chemical stability. They consequently accumulate in environments and along food chains, are distributed by wind and water in the biosphere, and persist in foods that reach man. Their effects on physiological processes may be varied, but the best known substance, DDT, acts on the central nervous system to produce tremors and convulsions. DDT is accumulated in fatty tissues, and may be withdrawn from them into the blood stream with lethal effects when fat reserves are utilized by the organism. Aquatic, as well as terrestrial, organisms are highly sensitive to chlorinated hydrocarbons. Vulnerableness to chlorinated hydrocarbons is shared by invertebrate and vertebrate animals; birds and fish are highly vulnerable, mammals relatively less so. Because of wide use to control the insect pests of farm crops, the organophosphates, chlorinated hydrocarbons, and some other poisons are often referred to as pesticides.

The ecological behavior of these substances resembles that of radioisotopes in a number of ways. Many of the relationships discussed in the previous section apply, although one cannot simply relate pesticides to nontoxic relatives whose ecologic and metabolic routes they follow. Ecological significance of pesticides is strongly affected by their half lives of decay into inactive compounds. The organophosphates with short chemical half lives are of less ecological significance than the chlorinated hydrocarbons with long ones. As certain radioisotopes decay to yield another radioisotope, so some of the chlorinated hydrocarbons change chemically in the environment to other hydrocarbons, also toxic (aldrin–dieldrin, DDT–DDD–DDE). Like radioisotopes, pesticides are actively taken up through living membranes from the environment, or from the contents of digestive tracts. Concentration ratios of many thousand times from environment into organisms result and are part of the basis of their effectiveness as poisons used with purpose. Like radioisotopes the persistent pesticides are transferred along food chains. In some cases, though not all, concentration ratios increase along food chains to the tissues of vertebrate predators. Equilibria in animal tissues are affected by such factors as a compound's stability, food-chain relations if uptake is indirect, and turnover time in and metabolic treatment by the animal. Like the radioisotopes, the more stable pesticides are transported long distances at low concentrations in wind and water, to appear in biologically significant concentrations at points distant from those of their release.

DDT is one of the oldest and most widely used of these poisons, for which unintended dispersal and biological effects are best known. Some of the earliest observations of effects of chlorinated hydrocarbons involved the extensive death of robins and other birds in cities where trees had been sprayed with DDT in the effort to control Dutch elm disease. Bird populations in a number of cities were temporarily reduced by 30 to 90 per cent following elm spraying. Mortality is by no means limited to robins but may involve, with varying mortality levels, most or all of the bird species nesting and feeding in the sprayed area. The mortality of robins may be highest following rains, when earthworms are most abundant as food on the surface of the ground. The effects are based on a food-chain concentration process. DDT reaches the soil by the settling of the spray, with falling leaves (if these have been sprayed in summer), and probably by rain wash from leaf and bark surfaces to the soil. Earthworms may concentrate the DDT by factors of more than ten times from their food (decaying leaves and other soil materials) into their tissues. Some tissues of the robin concentrate the DDT further; levels of DDT and DDE with lethal effects on the nervous system of robins are easily reached with ordinary intensities of spraying. Deaths of birds that feed in the tree foliage rather than on the ground (warblers, orioles, and so on) indicate poisoning through other food chains than that of earthworms and robins.

Clear Lake is a popular recreational center that has had excellent sport fishing, about one hundred miles north of San Francisco. A midge (*Chaoborus*) that is related to mosquitoes but does not bite is so abundant at the lake as to be a nuisance. The chlorinated hydrocarbon DDD was applied to the lake at concentrations of one part DDD to 50 to 70 million parts of water in 1949, 1954, and 1957. The first and second applications killed about 99 per cent of the midges, but in each case the midge population recovered rapidly in the years following the DDD application. The DDD further caused extensive mortality and tissue contamination of other invertebrate animals in the lake, and consequently of the birds and fish feeding on these. A colony of one thousand western grebes that bred at the lake disappeared from it, and extensive mortality has been observed in grebes visiting the lake in winter, after breeding in other areas. A DDD level of 1,600 ppm. was found in visceral fat of these grebes from the lake; high levels were recorded in some hundreds of other samples, including plankton, fish, frogs, and birds. DDD is less toxic to fish than DDT, but the range of DDD in fatty tissues of fish was 40 to 2,500 ppm. Concentration in edible flesh of fish was less high (1 to 200 ppm., predominantly above 20) but was higher in predatory fish favored as human food than in herbivorous species. Flesh of most fish exceeded the maximum tolerance level of 7 ppm. set by the Food and Drug Administration for DDD residues in marketed foods. Concentration ratios for DDD in the lake were about 265 times from water into plankton, 500 times into small fishes, up to 80,000 times into the fat of grebes, and 85,000 times into the fat of predatory fishes. The third application of DDD produced only limited and brief reduction of the midge populations (suggesting evolution of resistance), and the effort at control by DDD was abandoned as unsuccessful. Pesticide residues in, and damage to, the lake persist.

DDT has now achieved world-wide distribution in the biosphere. Although of low solubility, DDT is carried by moving water into streams and lakes, and from these into the oceans. In addition the talc dust that is used for aerial spraying with DDT has now become probably world-wide in the manner of radioactive dusts; it has been found as the principal dust component in air samples from over Pacific islands. Some marine bird and fish individuals on the Antarctic Coast, most remote in the world from major agricultural areas, have low levels of DDT and DDE in their tissues, as do many animals of the open oceans. Pesticide residues occur very widely in terrestrial vertebrates. Widespread population declines have been observed in some species of predatory birds in the United States and Europe and are attributed primarily to pesticide poisoning. Population declines have affected both species that rely on terrestrial food chains (peregrine falcon, European sparrow hawk) and those with aquatic food chains (osprey, bald eagle, pelican). Mortality and extinction in natural populations may be gradual effects of lower levels of tissue contamination with pesticides than those producing tremors and death in adults. Population decline is believed to occur by less obvious processes— effects on the endocrine system that interfere with reproductive behavior in adult birds, result in thin-shelled and frequently broken eggs, and reduce survival of embryos and young birds. There may also be increase in relative mortality of adults at times of hunger stress, when DDT is released from fat into the blood.

Despite the ecological consequences of pesticides that are now widely recognized, their use has increased by an accelerating curve. Certain chlorinated hydrocarbons, the polychlorinated biphenyls, are widely used in the plastics industry and are now widespread contaminants in environment and the tissues of birds and other organisms. Production of DDT in the United States has declined since 1964, and there has been some shift of emphasis in use of pesticides away from the chlorinated hydrocarbons and toward the less persistent organophosphates. In the world as a whole production and use of the chlorinated hydrocarbons as a group is still rapidly increasing. Further accumulation in the environment and more extensive wildlife mortality must be expected. Adequate data on the accumulation rate and residence time of pesticides in the oceans are not yet available. Their persent occurrence in the ocean, combined with the continuing accumulation from streams draining into the ocean (and probably by the settling of dust into the ocean) should imply population decline and extinction for vulnerable marine species. Such effects should appear first on the continental shelves and in marine birds and in fish that are top carnivores—the species most used as food by man. Apart from mortality, pesticide contamination may render fish unsuitable for human food. Coho salmon from Lake Michigan have recently (1969) been found to contain DDT at 4–6 times the tolerance standard for sale and human consumption.

Chlorinated hydrocarbons have been of great value in agriculture. They often provide dependable, persistent, and relatively complete control of insect pests with less expense, effort, and biological skill and understanding than are needed in the use of resistant strains of crops, natural enemies of pests, and other chemical agents. In many cases, however, a pesticide application destroys the population of a predator or parasite (that controls a pest population) more effectively than it destroys the pest population itself. Increased likelihood of a damaging outbreak of the pest results, requiring continued pesticide use to maintain control. In some cases control of the pest by pesticide releases the population of an alternative, more resistant pest, requiring additional control measures.

In California citrus orchards the cottony cushion scale insect had been effectively controlled by natural enemies, notably the vedalia beetle. DDT was much more toxic to the beetle than to the scale insects, and its use led not to increased control but to outbreaks of the pest. In a number of areas control of insect pests with pesticides has led to emergence from obscurity of mites, more resistant to the poisons, as new and serious pests. Survival of more resistant individuals in a pest population treated with pesticide can produce rapid evolution of a more resistant population. Increased intensity of application or introduction of new poisons may be needed to maintain control.

Pesticide contents of foods are subject to legal limits and controls. It is necessarily the case, however, that pesticides circulate from agricultural application back through food, and probably also water and the atmosphere, to man himself. All of us carry small amounts of these poisons in our tissues. So far as is known there is no present reason for concern for human health in general. Tissue levels in man are (if cases of intense exposure in agricultural areas are excluded) much below those that produce short-term physiological effects of toxicity. Grounds for long-range confidence regarding effects on human health are less secure. Effects of chronic exposure to low levels of varied mixtures of pesticides in tissues are wholly unknown. Pesticide contamination in environment and foods will increase, but the levels to which the contamination will increase cannot be effectively predicted. Our ignorance now of the long-term implications of these poisons for human health equals our ignorance thirty years ago of the long-term effects of radio-isotopes, atmospheric pollution, and cigarette smoke.

Lake Production and Eutrophication

It is possible to arrange many lakes along a gradient from *oligotrophic* lakes, with low nutrient content in the water and low productivity, to *eutrophic* lakes, with high nutrient levels and productivity. Because of the many features of lakes that are not interdependent, such a gradient is a simplification. It serves, however, to relate some characteristics of lakes in ways that are appropriate to our present concern. As in the oceans, the productivity of lakes is determined in large part by amounts, rates, and characters of nutrient circulations. A number of factors affect the nutrient circulation of lakes.

1. Fertility of the drainage basin. Of two lakes, one receiving inflowing water from an area of infertile rocks (quartzite or granite mountains, say), the other from an area of fertile soils (as of a rich farming area on limestone), the latter should be the more productive. Continuing input of greater quantities of nutrients maintains larger pools of circulating nutrients as a basis of productivity.

2. Lake depth and slope of shore. Comparing two lakes, one deep with steep, rocky shores, the other shallow with sloping shores of mud and sand, the latter should be the more productive. In the first most of the bottom is out of reach of sunlight, and plants cannot grow on the bottom and contribute to the lake's production. The fact that the lake is deep may imply also that thermal stratification prevents effective movement of nutrients from the depths of the lake into the lighted surface waters during much of the warm season. The steep, rocky shores imply that shallows and the growth of plants along the shore are limited. In the shallow lake extensive

growth of shore and bottom plants adds their productivity to that of the plankton. Furthermore, the shore and bottom plants support the productivity of the plankton itself by releasing organic matter and nutrients into the lighted surface waters. It is thus to be expected that the productivity of shallow lakes will be higher—not merely in terms of productivity per unit of water volume, but in production per unit of the lake's surface area.

3. Form of shoreline. Closely related to the preceding is the form of the shoreline. Of two lakes with similar size, depth, and slope of the shores, the lake with a long and irregular shoreline with many inlets should have greater productivity than one with a short shoreline. The longer shoreline implies a greater area of production by the shore plants relative to the area of the lake. High productivity is thus favored both by low ratio of depth to area and by high ratio of shore length to area.

4. Temperature. Of two lakes of similar shape and size, that of the warmer climate has the longer season of biological activity and greater nutrient turnover through the year, and the higher production. Temperature is thus one basis (though not the only one) for the contrast between some oligotrophic mountain lakes of very low productivity and crystal water, and some eutrophic lowland lakes of high productivity and more turbid waters.

5. Age. Most lakes are relatively short-lived, many were formed by glaciers and are only a few thousand years old. (There are some notable exceptions in large, deep, old, biologically distinctive lakes.) The lakes age in time as sediments are brought in and, along with organic materials from the lake itself, accumulate on the lake's bottom. The lake basin gradually fills, and the lake becomes shallower and its shores less steep. The lake may progress in time from the deep, steep-shored form of many oligotrophic lakes, to the shallow, sloping-shored form of typical eutrophic lakes (Figure 5·7). The lake ages, and the rate of this aging under natural conditions is determined by the fertility of its drainage basin, the form of the lake basin, the temperature, and the input of sediments. Given time, the progression may lead from a shallow lake to a marsh or swamp and thence to dry land. The lake ages from relatively oligotrophic youth through eutrophic maturity to senescence and disappearance. Because the aging process includes a development from an oligotrophic toward a eutrophic condition, the process may be termed *eutrophication*.

Man has his own uses for the shores of lakes and of the streams that drain into them. From settlements, cities, and industries water that has been used or affected by man drains into water bodies. Some reaches

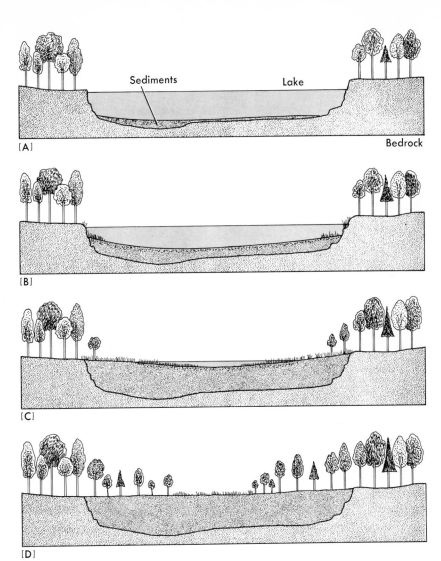

Figure 5·7. Filling and aging of a lake. A: The lake is recently formed and deep, with steep, rocky walls. The water is very clear, and productivity is low, with a sparse plankton, no shore vegetation, and no bottom algae. Sediments, primarily silt brought in by streams, are beginning to accumulate on the bottom. **B:** The lake has accumulated substantial sediments and is partly filled, and the rock walls have eroded and are less steep. There is some shore vegetation and bottom algae, and productivity and nutrient content of the water are higher. **C:** The lake is senescent, largely filled by silt and organic sediments. The shores are on gradually sloping sediments; there are extensive marshes and shore vegetation, and algae occur over most of the bottom area. Productivity of the much reduced volume of water is still high. **D:** Filling of the lake and its occupation by terrestrial vegetation are completed. A small central marsh is the only remnant of the lake in an area of forest.

of streams are turned into sewage channels, or into aquatic deserts by toxic products of industry, and lakes receive pollutants both from streams and from their own shores. Although some industrial wastes are toxic, the more widespread problem is pollution with organic wastes and nutrients that are not inherently toxic. Large amounts of nutrients, however, accelerate the eutrophication of lakes. Especially when combined with the input of sewage or other organic material, large amounts of nutrients do not produce a favorable increase in the natural productivity of the lake, but a distorted, unbalanced, and unfavorable increase in productivity.

The power of these processes to change the quality of lakes is illustrated by the recent history of a large American lake, Lake Erie. Eutrophication is expressed in the curve of dissolved solids in the lake water, Figure 5·8. The water itself has become increasingly malodorous, unpalatable, and unacceptable for swimming. Windrows of decaying

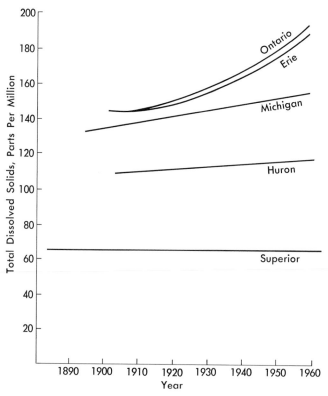

Figure 5·8. Eutrophication of Lake Erie and other Great Lakes as reflected in total dissolved solids in the water. Lakes Erie and Ontario have shown rapid eutrophication effects in the last thirty years, Lakes Michigan and Huron less striking ones. Lake Superior is more strongly oligotrophic than the other lakes and has not yet been affected by eutrophication. [Beeton, 1965.]

algae and great numbers of dead fish are at times cast up on the shore. The natural bottom communities of animals are transformed in some areas and replaced by forms tolerant of pollution. Desirable commercial food fish formerly harvested from the lake—20 million pounds of cisco, 15 of blue pike, 2 of whitefish, and so on—have largely disappeared to be replaced by less desirable rough fish. The lake drains through Niagara Falls, and to the visual beauty and aural impressiveness of the great falls is now added a third, less welcome sensation, the scent of pollution.

Through Niagara Falls the water of Lake Erie reaches Lake Ontario, now also subject to eutrophication. Effects are observed also in the larger Lake Michigan, especially at the southern end influenced by the Chicago metropolitan area. In smaller lakes where input of pollutants can be controlled, the abnormal eutrophication can be reversed. At Lake Washington, at Seattle, a combination of scientific research, aroused concern, civic foresight, and effective reduction of sewage input have produced recovery from the pollution once observed. It is unlikely that the increasing and unfavorable eutrophication of Lake Erie and the other Great Lakes, with massive and diverse pollution inputs from an area of major and increasing concentration of population and industry, can now be reversed.

Eutrophication is one of those processes that become increasingly widespread and rapid with the increase of human populations. As the population of the United States increases, these influences bear simultaneously on lakes: (1) increasing input of sewage from towns and cities, (2) increasing input of industrial wastes, some toxic, some occurring as organic wastes, some including inorganic nutrients, (3) increasingly intensive farming with heavy use of fertilizers, some of which must move into streams and lakes as nutrients supporting eutrophication, and (4) increasing domestic wastes other than sewage, notably detergents. Earlier detergents were resistant to biological decomposition and caused foaming and toxic effects in water bodies they reached. These detergents were replaced with degradable ones; the latter release phosphates in amounts that contribute to eutrophication. The first two sources of eutrophication are soluble in principle, but the expense of such solution is so great as to render it difficult or unattainable on a widespread basis. The last two are illustrations of technology's left hand—the adverse environmental effects of technology that is favorable in its own sphere.

Atmospheric Pollution

The sinistral effects of technology appear also in atmospheric pollution. The wealth of energy used, which is the real basis of the industrial wealth of the advanced nations, is based largely on the burning of fossil fuels—coal and petroleum products. Like all energy conversions this burning is an imperfect process. Different combustion processes release varying amounts of unoxidized and incompletely oxidized hydrocarbons into the atmosphere along with toxic inorganic oxides—CO, NO, NO_2, and SO_2. Photochemical reactions in the atmosphere in sunlight produce other carbon and nitrogen compounds, and ozone (O_3).

As in other pollution processes, both local and general, acute and chronic, effects are observed. The toxic products of combustion from a city or industrial area are normally mixed upward into a large volume of air, without a hazard to man resulting. When air is held beneath an atmospheric inversion, particularly if it is also confined within a valley or basin ringed by mountains, hazardous levels of pollution may result. An early atmospheric pollution crisis in the United States occurred at Donora, Pennsylvania. The town and a local concentration of industry are situated in a horseshoe-shaped valley. In October, 1948, in a period when an inversion prevented dispersal of industrial fumes, these fumes accumulated until some 40 per cent of the population were made ill and twenty people killed.

One of the world's major pollution problems occurs in the Los Angeles Basin, California, and is produced by the combination of a large city and its suburbs with very heavy automobile traffic, frequent inversions, and mountains inland from the city. Combustion products in the air are acted on by sunlight to produce a distinctive smog, which at worst is both directly unpleasant, causing eye irritation and mild nausea, and a longer-range health hazard, as indicated in the increased frequency of emphysema and other respiratory ailments. Smog in Los Angeles and elsewhere includes potentially carcinogenic compounds; the relation of these to cancer incidence is, however, difficult to establish. Los Angeles smog prevents growth of some agricultural crops in the Basin and is killing pine trees in the mountains above the city, and it is probably affecting some other plant and animal life. Limitations on industrial pollution in the Los Angeles Basin and efforts at reduction of the release of pollutants by automobiles have been necessary, but the extent of the Los Angeles smog is still rapidly increasing. Visible smog from the Los Angeles area now spreads into all the valleys surrounding the Basin and at times extends, with densities decreasing with distance, across the deserts inland from the city into Arizona and Nevada. Automobiles are believed to be the source of more than half the combustion pollutants in the United States, and in the Los Angeles Basin 80 to 90 per cent.

New York City is not ringed by mountains but is part of a large area of industry, population, and automobile traffic. The city has chronic atmospheric pollution, which may be on a level with that of Los Angeles, depending on the kinds of measurements used to judge the degree of pollution. A period of acute pollution effects occurred from November 12 to 22, 1953, when a stagnant air mass covered the industrialized northeastern states. In addition to the direct irritation of the smog in New York City, later statistical analysis indicated an increase in death rate in the city during and following the pollution period amounting to between 175 and 260 deaths beyond those that would be normal for the period. Pollution comparable with that of Los Angeles and New York affects major urban and industrial areas in Europe and Japan, and smog occurs in many smaller communities around the world. As seen from the air, smog is of increasingly wide geographic extent, as well as of increasing local intensity.

Atmospheric pollution is thus in transition from a local problem to a phenomenon of the biosphere. The effect is best established for the major combustion product, carbon dioxide. The biogeochemical cycle for carbon is illustrated in Figure 5·9. One transfer rate, from fossil fuels to atmospheric CO_2, is enormously increased by man's combustion. A rate value now above 3.5 $g/m^2/yr$ implies the release of 9×10^9 metric tons (2×10^{13} lbs) of CO_2 into the atmosphere per year beyond the amount released by respiration and other routes before the time of industrial man. Major shifts in rate values imply shifts in pool magnitudes in such a system. The relatively small pool of CO_2 in the atmosphere is in exchange equilibrium with the much larger pool of CO_2 and carbonates in the ocean. The oceanic CO_2 and carbonates act as a buffering system that reduces the effect of combustion in raising atmospheric CO_2 levels. Nevertheless, the mean CO_2 content of the atmosphere is believed to have risen from 290 ppm. in 1900 to 330 ppm. by volume in 1960.

CO_2 contributes to the greenhouse effect of the atmosphere. This effect is the capacity of the atmosphere to transmit heat energy from the sun to the earth's surface, but to absorb heat energy in different wavelengths radiating from the earth's surface and to return some of this heat by reradiation back to the earth's surface. Increased CO_2 content of the atmosphere may thus imply the strengthening of the greenhouse effect and the warming of the earth's surface. A modest effect of CO_2 increase on mean temperatures of the earth's climates has probably occurred. It is not yet possible to project long-range implications effectively or to assess the possibility that higher temperatures might, by melting polar ice caps, increase the depth of ocean waters until coastal cities around the world are submerged. It is possible also that the rapidly increasing concentration of particles (smoke, dust, talc powder, and so on) in the atmosphere will, because these particles reflect sunlight, lower temperatures at the earth's surface in the future. Neither the carbon dioxide release nor the increase of atmospheric particles can easily be reversed now if the climatic consequences prove

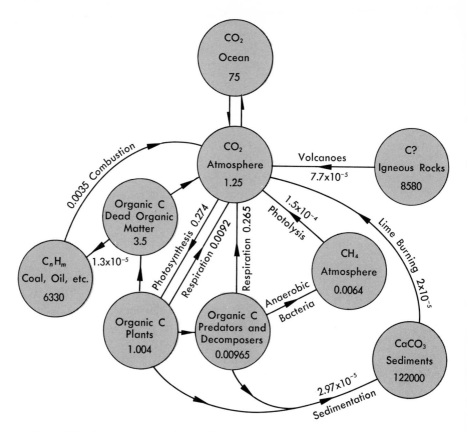

Figure 5·9. The biogeochemical cycle for carbon. Numbers in circles are amounts of carbon in pools, in kilograms per square meter of the earth's surface; numbers on arrows are transfer rates in kilograms of carbon per square meter per year. [Bowen, 1966.]

detrimental. It is indicative of man's inability either to predict adequately or to control his effects on environment that we do not yet know whether the net effect of pollution of the atmosphere will warm or cool the earth's surface or how serious the climatic effects will be.

Contributions of man's combustion to the atmosphere include also 2.8×10^8 t/yr of carbon monoxide, 7.7×10^7 t/yr of sulphur dioxide, and 2.3×10^7 t/yr of smoke particles. Pollutants are removed from the atmosphere by chemical changes, by settling in particles, and in solution in rain. Despite this removal, as rates of input of pollutants into the atmosphere increase, the magnitudes of the pools of pollutants in the atmosphere must increase. Although the residence times of CO and SO_2 in the atmosphere (probably three to four months, and between one and four days) are shorter than that for CO_2 (four years), these substances are also now global pollutants. Lead, released in the combustion of gasoline with "ethyl" (tetraethyl lead), is a global, and potentially toxic pollutant. Asbestos particles which wear off the brakes of cars, and magnesium from industrial and agricultural uses, are widespread and toxic pollutants. Some of the hydrocarbons of combustion and atmospheric photochemical reactions are probably also attaining global distribution.

Local and general atmospheric pollution are subject to a characteristic reinforcement relationship. Air moves around the earth in periods of fifteen to twenty-five days in mid latitudes. Pollutants from multiple local sources accumulate, to levels determined by input rate and residence time, as the air passes urban and industrial areas in circling the earth. Pollutants released in Los Angeles are thus added on top of pollutants from around the world, including Los Angeles. Even as local pollution increases the general pollution level, so the general pollution level increases the intensity of local pollution effects.

There is no evidence that human health is as yet significantly affected by levels of general pollution outside urban areas, but this fact is not strong reassurance. Despite the increasing use of nuclear fuels, very large expansion in the combustion of fossil fuels is to be expected in the future (Figure 5·10). The importance of local pollution control

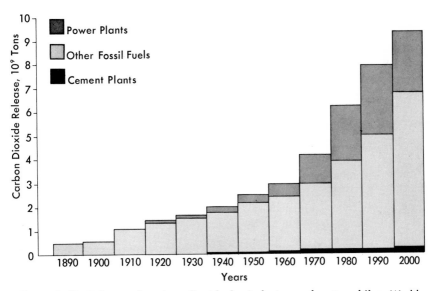

Figure 5·10. Release of carbon dioxide by industry and automobiles. World-wide totals in billions of tons per year. [Rohrman et al., *Science*, **156**:931, 1967.] Despite increasing use of nuclear power, realistic projections indicate rapidly increasing use of fossil fuels also through the remainder of the century.

as a means of reducing both local and general pollution effects should be clear.

Summary

The function of ecosystems includes a kind of metabolism—complex patterns of transfer, transformation, utilization, and accumulation of inorganic and organic materials. Three major groups of substances—inorganic nutrients, organic foods, and other chemical agents—are transferred between organisms and environment to give ecosystems their functional unity. In many eocsystems chemical function may be described in part by steady-state patterns of interrelated transfer rates and pool magnitudes for the different substances. There are marked similarities in designs of these patterns, but also marked differences in details and rate values, from one substance and ecosystem to another.

Substances are transferred between, as well as within, local ecosystems. The biosphere—the ecosystem of the earth's air, water, soil, and organisms—is an arena of moving currents of air and water and moving organisms. Nutrient circulations of land and water ecosystems are coupled by the transfer of nutrients from the land to the sea in rivers, and from the sea to the land by a shorter route from sea-spray into the atmosphere and onto the land by precipitation, and a longer route into the ocean sediments and onto land by elevation and exposure of these. Ecosystems of the world are thus linked together in biogeochemical cycles, patterns of transfer and concentration of substances in the biosphere and surface rocks. Chemical characteristics of the atmosphere, the soil, and the ocean waters are determined or strongly influenced by the activities of organisms.

Pollution effects of man are to be understood through ecosystem function and biogeochemical patterns. When pollutants are released into an ecosystem they may be concentrated many thousand times into organisms and along food chains, from low levels in environment to high and potentially toxic levels in organisms. At the same time pollutants are transferred between ecosystems in varied, and sometimes unforeseen, ways. Hazards from pollutants thus result from combinations of ecosystem function and biogeochemical transfer. Some of man's pollution effects involve the acceleration of movements along biogeochemical routes. Disparate effects of this sort include eutrophication of lakes by accelerated movement of nutrients into water bodies, and the increase of atmospheric carbon dioxide levels by combustion.

With the accelerating increase in human populations and technology a variety of substances, some toxic, are no longer diluted so as to disappear in air and water, but are accumulating as general pollutants of the biosphere. Marked parallels affect the biogeochemical behavior of different pollutants, including three classes of major concern and potential hazard for the human future—radioisotopes, pesticides, and combustion products.

References

Bowen, H. J. M. (1966) *Trace Elements in Biochemistry.* London and New York: Academic Press. ix + 241 pp.

Bresler, Jack B., editor. (1968) *Environments of Man.* (anthology). Reading, Mass.: Addison-Wesley. xi + 289 pp.

Commoner, Barry. (1963) *Science and Survival.* Reprint 1967, New York: Viking. 150 pp.

Environmental Pollution Panel, President's Science Advisory Committee. (1965) *Restoring the Quality of Our Environment.* Washington: Superintendent of Documents. xii + 317 pp.

Goldman, Marshall I., editor. (1967) *Controlling Pollution: The Economics of a Cleaner America.* (anthology). Englewood Cliffs, N.J.: Prentice-Hall. xiii + 175 pp.

Hynes, H. B. N. (1960) *The Biology of Polluted Waters.* Liverpool: University Press. xiv + 202 pp.

Lewis, Howard R. (1965) *With Every Breath You Take.* New York: Crown. xvii + 322 pp.

Mellanby, Kenneth. (1967) *Pesticides and Pollution.* London: Collins. 221 pp.

Odum, Eugene P., and H. T. Odum. (1959) *Fundamentals of Ecology.* 2nd ed. Philadelphia and London: Saunders. xvii + 546 pp.

Polikarpov, G. G. (1966) *Radioecology of Aquatic Organisms.* Transl. ed. by V. Schultz and A. W. Klement, Jr. New York: Reinhold. xxviii + 314 pp.

Rodin, L. E., and N. I. Bazilevich. (1968) *Production and Mineral Cycling in Terrestrial Vegetation.* Transl. ed. by G. E. Fogg. Edinburgh: Oliver & Boyd. v + 288 pp.

Rudd, Robert L. (1964) *Pesticides and the Living Landscape.* Madison: University of Wisconsin. xiv + 320 pp.

Wilson, Billy Ray, editor. (1968) *Environmental Problems: Pesticides, Thermal Pollution, and Environmental Synergisms.* Philadelphia and Toronto: Lippincott. 183 pp.

Bazilevič, N. I., and L. E. Rodin. (1966) "The biological cycle of nitrogen and ash elements in plant communities of the tropical and subtropical zones." *Forestry Abstracts,* **27**:357–368.

Beeton, A. M. (1965) "Eutrophication of the St. Lawrence Great Lakes." *Limnology and Oceanography,* **10**:240–254.

Bormann, F. H., and G. E. Likens. (1967) "Nutrient Cycling." *Science,* **155**:424–429.

Chapman, S. B. (1967) "Nutrient budgets for a dry health ecosystem in the South of England." *Journal of Ecology,* 55:677–689.

Cole, L. C. (1958) "The ecosphere." *Scientific American,* 198 (no. 4, Apr.): 83–92.

Dixon, J. P., and J. P. Lodge. (1965) "Air conservation report reflects national concern." *Science,* 148:1060–1066.

Ehrlich, P. R., and P. H. Raven. (1965) "Butterflies and plants: a study in coevolution." *Evolution,* 18:586–608.

Eisner, T., and J. Meinwald. (1966) "Defensive secretions of arthropods." *Science,* 153:1341–1350.

Fraenkel, G. S. (1959) "The raison d'être of secondary plant substances." *Science,* 129:1466–1470.

Goldberg, E. D. (1963) "The oceans as a chemical system." In *The Sea,* M. N. Hill, editor. London: Interscience. Vol. 2, pp. 3–25.

Hayes, F. R., J. A. McCarter, M. L. Cameron, and D. A. Livingstone. (1952) "On the kinetics of phosphorus exchange in lakes." *Journal of Ecology,* 40:202–216.

Likens, G. E., F. H. Bormann, N. M. Johnson, and R. S. Pierce. (1967) "The calcium, magnesium, potassium, and sodium budgets for a small forested ecosystem." *Ecology,* 48:772–785.

Moore, N. W. (1967) "A synopsis of the pesticide problem." *Advances in Ecological Research,* 4:75–129.

Muller, C. H. (1966) "The role of chemical inhibition (allelopathy) in vegetational composition." *Bulletin of the Torrey Botanical Club,* 93:332–351.

Olson, J. S. (1963) "Energy storage and the balance of producers and decomposers in ecological systems." *Ecology,* 44:322–331.

Ovington, J. D. (1962) "Quantitative ecology and the woodland ecosystem concept." *Advances in Ecological Research,* 1:103–192.

Ovington, J. D. (1965) "Organic production, turnover and mineral cycling in woodlands." *Biological Reviews,* 40:295–336.

Reichle, D. E. (1967) "Radioisotope turnover and energy flow in terrestrial isopod populations." *Ecology,* 48:351–366.

Rigler, F. H. (1956) "A tracer study of the phosphorus cycle in lake water." *Ecology,* 37:550–562.

Stewart, W. D. P. (1967) "Nitrogen-fixing plants." *Science,* 158:1426–1432.

Whittaker, R. H. (1961) "Experiments with radiophosphorus tracer in aquarium microcosms." *Ecological Monographs,* 31:157–188.

Woodwell, G. M., C. F. Wurster, Jr., and P. A. Isaacson. (1967) "DDT residues in an East Coast estuary: a case of biological concentration of a persistent insecticide." *Science,* 156:821–824.

Wurster, C. F., Jr., and D. B. Wingate. (1968) "DDT residues and declining reproduction in the Bermuda petrel." *Science,* 159:979–981.

Conclusion: Human Ecology

THE POLLUTION PROBLEMS discussed may (along with overgrazing, erosion, and some other effects of man's activities) be collected under a common term—environmental degradation. The biosphere is man's environment. The relations of human populations to environment, their effects in changing environment, and the effects of the changes in environment on human beings, are aspects of human ecology.

It is man's environment that man degrades, in minor and moderate ways when populations are low and technology simple, in major and serious ways when populations are high and technology powerful. Degradation processes are now occurring that are unplanned, uncontrolled, potentially hazardous, and accelerating. Man is a dominant population whose chemical pollutants imply widespread allelopathic suppression of other species. They imply also the approach of auto-toxic effects on man himself—in the form of some local pollution crises, but primarily of widespread statistical increase in human morbidity and mortality caused or influenced by chemicals in food and environment. Man's pollution may also be regarded as a great, uncontrolled experiment: to determine by experience what levels of concentration of what variety of chemicals in environment may be reached before effects on human health can be recognized.

Conservationists regret the loss of natural areas to land development and of wildlife to pesticides and other disturbances. The natural areas and wildlife have aesthetic, recreational, and scientific values that are sacrificed permanently, though for short-term purposes. Their loss is part of no strategy for a long-range solution of man's problems of population and environment. In the United States, in contrast to some of the European countries, spreading development occupies without restraint agricultural land, range land, and open and recreational land. Increasing population makes it likely that this use of land will be regretted as a refusal of foresight, a national nonpolicy. Ospreys and pine trees affected by pesticides and smog are man's own vanguard; their experiences warn of chemical effects on environment that (if population growth and technology continue on their present course) can hardly fail in time to affect man himself.

Escape from control can be a gratification to an individual and a catastrophe to a population. Much is written about the human population problem, but much of what needs to be said is stated by Figure 6·1. It is this steepening curve that casts across our time a curvilinear

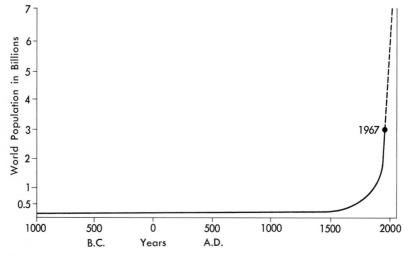

Figure 6·1. Growth of the human population through three millennia. The dramatic steepening of growth in the last three centuries coincides with the Industrial and Medical Revolutions; reasonable projection implies a population around 7 billion by the year 2,000 [Dorn, 1962.]

shadow of increasing problems and hazard in the relations of man to environment and of nations to one another. Three broad areas of problems are involved. The first of these is the growth of human populations beyond the food supplies to support them. Since the Second World War the rate of increase of food production in the world at large has fallen behind the rate of population growth. No sustained reversal of this trend (warnings of which were stated in the 1940's and 1950's) is yet in prospect, and famines in some areas in the decade 1970–1980 are predicted. New advances in agriculture may postpone famine as such, but cannot (with continued population growth) solve the poor countries' long-term problems of hunger and poverty.

The second is environmental degradation with its implications of increasing exposure to pollution, reduction of the productivity of some ecosystems, and destruction and crowding of open space. The third comprises effects of population problems on human psychology, effects that in different countries variously involve famine and its prospect, awareness of deepening national poverty, submergence of the individual in very large urban areas and social systems uninfluenced by him, decline (because of crowding and the dissolution of traditional culture and value systems) of tolerance and willing self-restraint, concentration of population in cities of increasing poverty and pollution, and discouragement before the population problem itself. Such effects contribute to the politics of anger; and the effects may be no less important for the impossibility of measuring their significance and balancing this against beneficial aspects of urban life.

Of these areas of problems the first and last are very much a part of human ecology, but lie outside the concern of this text. The manner in which the three areas of problems interact and intensify one another's effects should, however, be observed, along with the wide differences in the manners in which they apply to different countries. The United States, fortunate among nations in so many respects, is believed to face no real shortage of food, or space, or most essential industrial resources in the present century. This fact may make difficult a response to other real, if more complex and less easily measured, penalties of population growth. It is often not recognized that the warnings of Thomas Malthus and others on the consequences of population growth have indeed been fulfilled, but not in quite the ways expected. For the poor countries overpopulation has in general produced not acute, catastrophic famine, but chronic, marginal famine and inescapable poverty. For the rich countries overpopulation now implies not famine but increasingly unmanageable environmental degradation and psychological effects.

Despite the complexities of these phenomena, certain common characteristics may be outlined.

1. The problems in their present forms are rooted in the growth of human populations. There is an earlier time in a nation's history when population growth seems to aid in the development of a land for human benefit. There is a later time when population growth both creates ever more new problems and renders new problems and old ones ever more difficult of solution. The United States and many other nations are now in the latter time.

2. Many of the problems are based on a partnership of population growth and technology. In a sparsely settled world of limited technology, adverse effects of technology are local and mostly minor.

In a densely settled world of powerful technology, unforeseen adverse effects of technology are normal, and some of these are widespread and far from minor. The United States is now at a stage where technology both creates new problems and, by making possible the support of still larger populations, intensifies the problems to be faced later.

3. For both these reasons most of the problems are subject to geometrically accelerating aggravation.

4. The problems are ecological in character, involving interactions of populations (man's) with environment, with complex functional systems (human communities and the biosphere) on both sides of the interaction. Such problems are generally not, when the problems are well advanced, subject to easy solution by treatment of symptoms.

5. The consequences of technology are the cumulative effects of many acts that are not individually objectionable. Many effects of technology on environment are not predictable from the direct consequences of these individual acts. Cumulative and indirect effects, unforeseen in detail, emerge with experience.

6. It is consequently difficult to regulate individual applications of technology. The reasons for the regulation are not clear, direct, and immediate detriment but cumulative, future, and apparently remote detriment. There is no evident responsibility of the individual act for the cumulative effect, and it is accordingly difficult to impose restraints on individual acts.

7. It is difficult also, because of the problems' complexities and mixtures of adverse with favorable developments, to gain agreement on the need for solution through controls. Short-term fluctuations in food harvest divert attention from far more significant trends of overpopulation, malnutrition, and poverty. Hopes of easy technological solutions encourage unrealism about effects of both population growth and technological abuse, even though technology is now creating environmental problems more rapidly than solutions and the problems produced by population growth combined with expanding technology may be expected to become ever more intractable.

8. Because of all the preceding there is a tendency for the individual problems to overshoot: to reach an advanced stage before their gravity is recognized and to continue to advance with the impulsion of established practices after their gravity is recognized. Taken all together, consequences of population growth and environmental abuse are developing toward problems that may be too massive and diverse for any solution—toward probably irreversible entrapment.

These problems are collectively far more serious for the human future than any single current measurement will establish. They are also very difficult to solve. Beyond the short term they can be solved only by population stabilization combined with some technological restraints. Except for the experience of Japan, it has so far proved difficult to slow the growth of, and almost impossible to stabilize, human populations even when the need is greatest. It is for such reasons that pessimists judge that man may be trapped in his own population growth, that this growth is a relentless historic process that cannot be halted except by catastrophe, and that this growth must in the end destroy most of what Western man most values. The vanishing of the optimism of an earlier generation, the belief that the United States or the world could without penalty permit indefinite population growth and environmental abuse, is itself an advantage. Only by realism and effort commensurate with the difficulty may problems of human ecology be solved. It is on trust in such realism and effort, and the assumption of the possibility of controlling population level and environmental use by intelligence rather than tragedy, that a more hopeful outlook regarding the human future may be based.

It may be only realism to judge that the problems of human ecology are not now soluble without population control. Neither ecological understanding nor technological ingenuity can continue for long to provide sufficient answers for rapidly intensifying, interlocking problems. If, however, one can assume the development of restraints on population and technological abuse, then ecological knowledge can, along with technological resourcefulness, aid in the solution of environmental problems. Such is one of the objectives of ecology. These objectives include knowledge of adaptation and population process, appreciation and understanding of natural communities and the evolution of organisms in them, comprehension of the function of ecosystems and the biosphere, and contribution to a wiser and more understanding, long-term management of natural communities and environment in relation to human needs.

References

Boulding, Kenneth E. (1964) *The Meaning of the Twentieth Century, the Great Transition.* New York, Evanston, and London: Harper & Row. xvi + 199 pp.

Ehrlich, Paul R. (1968) *The Population Bomb.* New York: Ballantine. 223 pp.

Hardin, Garrett J., editor. (1969) *Population, Evolution, and Birth Control: A Collage of Controversial Readings,* 2nd ed. San Francisco: Freeman. xvi + 386 pp.

Johnson, Cecil E., editor. (1968) *Social and Natural Biology: Selections from Contemporary Classics.* Princeton, N.J.: Van Nostrand. xiii + 272 pp.

Kahn, Herman, and Anthony J. Wiener. (1967) *The Year 2000: A Framework for Speculation on the Next Thirty-Three Years.* New York and London: Macmillan. xxviii + 431 pp.

Muller, Herbert J. (1952) *The Uses of the Past: Profiles of Former Societies.* Reprint 1957, New York: Oxford University. xi + 394 pp.

Paddock, William, and Paul Paddock. (1967) *Famine—1975! America's Decision: Who Will Survive?* Boston and Toronto: Little, Brown. x + 276 pp.

Shepard, Paul, and Daniel McKinley, editors. (1969) *The Subversive Science: Essays Toward an Ecology of Man.* Boston: Houghton Mifflin. x + 453 pp.

Watt, Kenneth E. F. (1968) *Ecology and Resource Management.* New York: McGraw-Hill. xii + 450 pp.

Brown, H. (1967) "The combustibility of humans." *Saturday Review.* June 24, 1967. pp. 14–17, 66.

Davis, K. (1967) "Population policy: will current programs succeed?" *Science,* **158**:730–739.

Dorn, H. F. (1962) "World population growth: an international dilemma." *Science,* **135**:283–290.

Foerster, H. von, P. M. Mora, and L. W. Amiot. (1960) "Doomsday: Friday, 13 November, A. D. 2026." *Science,* **132**:1291–1295.

Tinbergen, N. (1968) "On war and peace in animals and man." *Science,* **160**:1411–1418.

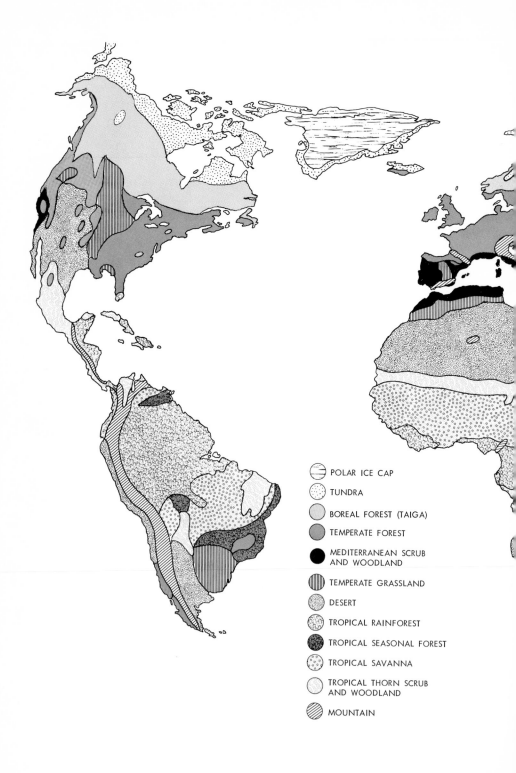

POLAR ICE CAP

TUNDRA

BOREAL FOREST (TAIGA)

TEMPERATE FOREST

MEDITERRANEAN SCRUB
AND WOODLAND

TEMPERATE GRASSLAND

DESERT

TROPICAL RAINFOREST

TROPICAL SEASONAL FOREST

TROPICAL SAVANNA

TROPICAL THORN SCRUB
AND WOODLAND

MOUNTAIN

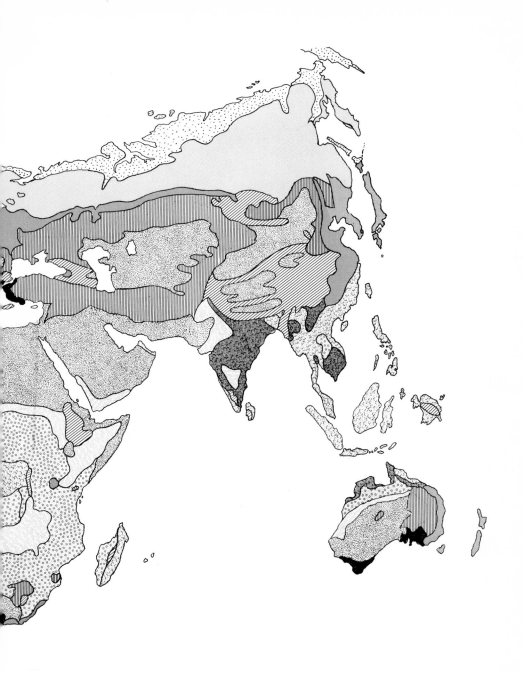

Index

157